Teacher's Lab Resource

Forces and Energy

interactive SCIENCE

PEARSON

Boston, Massachusetts Chandler, Arizona Glenview, Illinois Upper Saddle River, New Jersey

Safety Reviewers

W. H. Breazeale, Ph.D.
Department of Chemistry
College of Charleston
Charleston, South Carolina

Ruth Hathaway, Ph.D.
Hathaway Consulting
Cape Girardeau, Missouri

Douglas Mandt, M.S.
Science Education Consultant
Edgewood, Washington

Marie A. Ratliff
Science Assessment Specialist
Science Education Consultant
Smithville, Texas

Julie I. Wulff, Ph.D.
Adjunct Professor
National-Louis University
Buffalo Grove, Illinois

ISBN-13: 978-0-13-370539-3
ISBN-10: 0-13-370539-0
1 2 3 4 5 6 7 8 9 10 V084 13 12 11 10 09

Contents by Activity Type vi

Inquiry

Foundational Research: Inquiry in the Science Classroom ix

Master Materials List

Organized by Nonconsumables/Consumables xi

Student Safety Manual

Laboratory Safety Rules xxii
Safety Symbols........................xxiv
Laboratory Safety Contract xxvi
Student Safety Test xxvii
Laboratory Skills Checkup 1............xxxi
Laboratory Skills Checkup 2............xxxii
Laboratory Skills Checkup 3...........xxxiii
Laboratory Skills Checkup 4...........xxxiv
Laboratory Skills Checkup 5............xxxv

1 Motion

Table of Contents 1
Teacher Notes....................2

Describing Motion

Inquiry Warm-Up What Is Motion? 9
Quick Lab Identifying Motion............10

Speed and Velocity

Inquiry Warm-Up How Fast and How Far?..........................11
Lab Investigation Stopping on a Dime
Pre Lab 12
Directed Inquiry...................13
Open Inquiry 17
Quick Lab Velocity 21
Quick Lab Motion Graphs 22

Acceleration

Inquiry Warm-Up Will You Hurry Up? 23
Quick Lab Describing Acceleration 24
Quick Lab Graphing Acceleration 25

2 Forces

Table of Contents 26
Teacher Notes...................27

The Nature of Force

Inquiry Warm-Up Is the Force With You?..37
Quick Lab What Is Force?...............38
Quick Lab Modeling Unbalanced Forces..39

Friction and Gravity

Inquiry Warm-Up Observing Friction.....40
Lab Investigation Sticky Sneakers
Pre Lab 41
Directed Inquiry...................42
Open Inquiry 46
Quick Lab Calculating 50

Newton's Laws of Motion

Inquiry Warm-Up What Changes Motion?.........................51
Quick Lab Around and Around 52
Quick Lab Newton's Second Law........53
Quick Lab Interpreting Illustrations 54

Momentum

Inquiry Warm-Up How Pushy Is a Straw?..55
Quick Lab Colliding Cars 56

Free Fall and Circular Motion

Inquiry Warm-Up What Makes an Object Move in a Circle?...................57
Quick Lab Which Lands First? 58
Quick Lab Orbiting Earth 59

3

Work and Machines

Table of Contents 60
Teacher Notes 61

Work and Power

Inquiry Warm-Up Pulling at an Angle 70
Quick Lab What Is Work? 71
Quick Lab Investigating Power 72

Understanding Machines

Inquiry Warm-Up Is It a Machine? 73
Quick Lab Going Up 74
Quick Lab Mechanical Advantage 75
Quick Lab Friction and Efficiency 76

Inclined Planes and Levers

Inquiry Warm-Up Inclined Planes and Levers 77
Lab Investigation Angling for Access
Pre Lab 78
Directed Inquiry 79
Open Inquiry 83
Quick Lab Modeling Levers 87

Putting Machines Together

Inquiry Warm-Up Machines That Turn 88
Quick Lab Building Pulleys 89
Quick Lab Machines in the Kitchen 90

4

Energy

Table of Contents 91
Teacher Notes 92

What Is Energy?

Inquiry Warm-Up How High Does a Ball Bounce? 99
Lab Investigation Can You Feel the Power?
Pre Lab 100
Directed Inquiry 101
Open Inquiry 105
Quick Lab Mass, Velocity, and Kinetic Energy 109

Forms of Energy

Inquiry Warm-Up What Makes a Flashlight Shine? 110
Quick Lab Determining Mechanical Energy 111
Quick Lab Sources of Energy 112

Energy Transformations and Conservation

Inquiry Warm-Up What Would Make a Card Jump? 113
Quick Lab Soaring Straws 114
Quick Lab Law of Conservation of Energy 115

5

Thermal Energy and Heat

Table of Contents 116
Teacher Notes 117

Temperature, Thermal Energy, and Heat

Inquiry Warm-Up How Cold Is the Water? 124
Lab Investigation Build Your Own Thermometer
Pre Lab 125
Directed Inquiry 126
Open Inquiry 130
Quick Lab Temperature and Thermal Energy 134

The Transfer of Heat

Inquiry Warm-Up What Does It Mean to Heat Up? 135
Quick Lab Visualizing Convection Currents 136

Thermal Properties

Inquiry Warm-Up Thermal Properties . . . 137
Quick Lab Frosty Balloons 138

6 Electricity

Table of Contents 139
Teacher Notes 140

Electric Charge and Static Electricity

Inquiry Warm-Up Can You Move a Can Without Touching It? 148
Quick Lab Drawing Conclusions 149
Quick Lab Sparks Are Flying 150

Electric Current

Inquiry Warm-Up How Can Current Be Measured? 151
Quick Lab Producing Electric Current . . . 152
Quick Lab Conductors and Insulators . . . 153
Quick Lab Modeling Potential Difference 154

Electric Circuits

Inquiry Warm-Up Do the Lights Keep Shining? 155
Quick Lab Ohm's Law 156
Lab Investigation Build a Flashlight
Pre Lab 157
Directed Inquiry 158
Open Inquiry 162

Electric Power and Safety

Inquiry Warm-Up How Can You Make a Bulb Burn More Brightly? 166
Quick Lab Calculating Electric Power and Energy Use 167
Quick Lab Electric Shock and Short Circuit Safety 168

7 Magnetism and Electromagnetism

Table of Contents 169
Teacher Notes 170

What Is Magnetism?

Inquiry Warm-Up Natural Magnets 182
Lab Investigation Detecting Fake Coins
Pre Lab 183
Directed Inquiry 184
Open Inquiry 188
Quick Lab Magnetic Poles 192

Magnetic Fields

Inquiry Warm-Up Predict the Field 193
Quick Lab Spinning in Circles 194
Quick Lab Earth's Magnetic Field 195

Electromagnetic Force

Inquiry Warm-Up Electromagnetism 196
Quick Lab Electric Current and Magnetism 197
Quick Lab Magnetic Fields From Electric Current 198
Quick Lab Electromagnet 199

Electricity, Magnetism, and Motion

Inquiry Warm-Up How Are Electricity, Magnets, and Motion Related? 200
Quick Lab Can a Magnet Move a Wire? . . 201
Quick Lab How Galvanometers Work . . . 202
Quick Lab Parts of an Electric Motor 203

Electricity From Magnetism

Inquiry Warm-Up Electric Current Without a Battery 204
Quick Lab Inducing an Electric Current . . 205
Quick Lab How Generators Work 206
Quick Lab How Transformers Work 207

SI Conversion Tables 208
Graph Paper 209
Answers to Student Safety Test 210

Inquiry Warm-Up

Can You Move a Can Without Touching It? . . . 148
Do the Lights Keep Shining? . . . 155
Electric Current Without a Battery . . . 204
Electromagnetism . . . 196
How Are Electricity, Magnets, and Motion Related? . . . 200
How Can Current Be Measured? . . . 151
How Can You Make a Bulb Burn More Brightly? . . . 166
How Cold Is the Water? . . . 124
How Fast and How Far? . . . 11
How High Does a Ball Bounce? . . . 99
How Pushy Is a Straw? . . . 55
Inclined Planes and Levers . . . 77
Is It a Machine? . . . 73
Is the Force With You? . . . 37
Machines That Turn . . . 88
Natural Magnets . . . 182
Observing Friction . . . 40
Predict the Field . . . 193
Pulling at an Angle . . . 70
Thermal Properties . . . 137
What Changes Motion? . . . 51
What Does It Mean to Heat Up? . . . 135
What Is Motion? . . . 9
What Makes a Flashlight Shine? . . . 110
What Makes an Object Move in a Circle? . . . 57
What Would Make a Card Jump? . . . 113
Will You Hurry Up? . . . 23

Quick Lab

Around and Around . . . 52
Building Pulleys . . . 89
Calculating . . . 50
Calculating Electric Power and Energy Use . . . 167
Can a Magnet Move a Wire? . . . 201
Colliding Cars . . . 56
Conductors and Insulators . . . 153
Describing Acceleration . . . 24

Quick Lab (continued)

Determining Mechanical Energy 111
Drawing Conclusions 149
Earth's Magnetic Field 195
Electric Current and Magnetism 197
Electric Shock and Short Circuit Safety 168
Electromagnet 199
Friction and Efficiency 76
Frosty Balloons 138
Going Up 74
Graphing Acceleration 25
How Galvanometers Work 202
How Generators Work 206
How Transformers Work 207
Identifying Motion 10
Inducing an Electric Current 205
Interpreting Illustrations 54
Investigating Power 72
Law of Conservation of Energy 115
Machines in the Kitchen 90
Magnetic Fields From Electric Current 198
Magnetic Poles 192
Mass, Velocity, and Kinetic Energy 109
Mechanical Advantage 75
Modeling Levers 87
Modeling Potential Difference 154
Modeling Unbalanced Forces 39
Motion Graphs 22
Newton's Second Law 53
Ohm's Law 156
Orbiting Earth 59
Parts of an Electric Motor 203
Producing Electric Current 152
Soaring Straws 114
Sources of Energy 112
Sparks Are Flying 150
Spinning in Circles 194

Quick Lab (continued)

Temperature and Thermal Energy 134
Velocity 21
Visualizing Convection Currents 136
What Is Force? 38
What Is Work? 71
Which Lands First? 58

Lab Investigation

Angling for Access
- Pre Lab 78
- Directed Inquiry 79
- Open Inquiry 83

Build a Flashlight
- Pre Lab 157
- Directed Inquiry 158
- Open Inquiry 162

Build Your Own Thermometer
- Pre Lab 125
- Directed Inquiry 126
- Open Inquiry 130

Can You Feel the Power?
- Pre Lab 100
- Directed Inquiry 101
- Open Inquiry 105

Detecting Fake Coins
- Pre Lab 183
- Directed Inquiry 184
- Open Inquiry 188

Sticky Sneakers
- Pre Lab 41
- Directed Inquiry 42
- Open Inquiry 46

Stopping on a Dime
- Pre Lab 12
- Directed Inquiry 13
- Open Inquiry 17

Foundational Research: Inquiry in the Science Classroom

"How do I know if my students are inquiring?" "If students are busy doing lots of hands-on activities, are they using inquiry?" "What is inquiry, anyway?" If you're confused, you're not alone. Inquiry is the heart and soul of science education, with most of us in continuous pursuit of achieving it with our students.

> "Because inquiry is an intellectual pursuit, it cannot merely be characterized by keeping students busy and active."
>
> —Michael J. Padilla
> Program Author of *Interactive Science*
> Professor of Science Education
> University of Georgia
> Athens, Georgia

Defining Science Inquiry

What is it? Simply put, inquiry is the intellectual side of science. It is thinking like a scientist—being inquisitive, asking why, and searching for answers. The National Science Education Content Standards define inquiry as the process in which students begin with a question, design an investigation, gather evidence, formulate an answer to the original question, and communicate the investigative process and results. Since it is often difficult to accomplish all this in one class period, the standards also acknowledge that at times students need to practice only one or two inquiry components.

Understanding Inquiry

The National Research Council in Inquiry and the National Science Education Standards (2000) identified several "essential features" of classroom inquiry. We have modified these essential features into questions to guide you in your quest for enhanced and more thoughtful student inquiry.

1. ***Who asks the question?*** In most curricula, these focusing questions are an element given in the materials. As a teacher, you can look for labs that, at least on a periodic basis, allow students to pursue their own questions.

2. ***Who designs the procedures?*** To gain experience with the logic underlying experimentation, students need continuous practice with designing procedures. Some labs in which the primary target is content acquisition designate procedures. But others should ask students to do so.

3. ***Who decides what data to collect?*** Students need practice in determining the data to collect.

4. ***Who formulates explanations based upon the data?*** Students should be challenged to think—to analyze and draw conclusions based on their data, not just copy answers from the text materials.

5. ***Who communicates and justifies the results?*** Activities should push students not only to communicate but also to justify their answers. Activities also should be thoughtfully designed and interesting so that students want to share their results and argue about conclusions.

Making Time for Inquiry

One last question—Must each and every activity have students do all of this?

The answer is an obvious and emphatic "No." You will find a great variety of activities in Interactive Science. Some activities focus on content acquisition, and thus they specify the question and most of the procedures. But many others stress in-depth inquiry from start to finish. Because inquiry is an intellectual pursuit, it cannot merely be characterized by keeping students busy and active. Too many students have a knack for being physically but not intellectually engaged in science. It is our job to keep them engaged intellectually.

Evaluator's Checklist

Ask yourself if your science program promotes inquiry by—

✔ Enabling students to pursue their own questions
✔ Allowing students to design their own procedures
✔ Letting students determine what data are best to collect
✔ Challenging students to think critically
✔ Pushing students to justify their answers

Interactive Science offers an abundance of activity options to suit your needs. Pearson has worked with Science Kit & Boreal Laboratories to develop Nonconsumable Kits and Consumable Kits that precisely match the needs of the *Interactive Science* labs. Use this Master Materials List or contact your local Pearson sales representative or Science Kit at 1-800-828-7777, or online at http://sciencekit.com. On the following pages, you'll find the materials listed by whether they are nonconsumable or consumable and in which activities the materials are used.

Nonconsumables

Description	Activity Title	Quantity per Class
Alligator clips with leads	Calculating Electric Power and Energy Use (QL) Conductors and Insulators (QL) Do the Lights Keep Shining? (IW) Electromagnetism (IW) How Can Current Be Measured? (IW) How Galvanometers Work (QL) Magnetic Fields From Electric Current (QL) Ohm's Law (QL) Parts of an Electric Motor (QL) Producing Electric Current (QL) Sources of Energy (QL)	24
* Balance	Calculating (QL) Soaring Straws (QL) Sticky Sneakers (LI)	5
* Ball, basketball	Law of Conservation of Energy (QL)	5
Ball, steel	Determining Mechanical Energy (QL)	5
Ball, table tennis	Around and Around (QL) Is It a Machine? (IW)	5
Ball, tennis	Graphing Acceleration (QL) How High Does a Ball Bounce? (IW) Identifying Motion (QL) Law of Conservation of Energy (QL)	5
Battery holder	Calculating Electric Power and Energy Use (QL) Conductors and Insulators (QL) Do the Lights Keep Shining? (IW) Electromagnet (QL) Electromagnetism (IW) How Can Current Be Measured? (IW) How Galvanometers Work (QL) Ohm's Law (QL) Parts of an Electric Motor (QL) Producing Electric Current (QL)	15
Beaker, 250-mL	How Galvanometers Work (QL) Thermal Properties (IW) Visualizing Convection Currents (QL)	20
Beaker, 600-mL	Build Your Own Thermometer (LI) What Does It Mean to Heat Up? (IW)	5
* Board	Angling for Access (LI) Can You Feel the Power? (LI) Electromagnetism (IW)	5
* Board, 1-m	Describing Acceleration (QL)	5

KEY:
* = School Supplied
Quantities based on five groups of six students per class.

Nonconsumables

Description	Activity Title	Quantity per Class
* Books	Angling for Access (LI) Calculating (QL) Can a Magnet Move a Wire? (QL) Can You Feel the Power? (LI) Describing Acceleration (QL) How Pushy Is a Straw? (IW) Is It a Machine? (IW) Mass, Velocity, and Kinetic Energy (QL) What Changes Motion? (IW)	
Bowl	Build Your Own Thermometer (LI) How Cold Is the Water? (IW)	15
* Calculator, solar	Can You Feel the Power? (LI) Sources of Energy (QL)	5
* Can opener	Is It a Machine? (IW)	1
Car, pull-back	Sources of Energy (QL) Velocity (QL) What Is Motion? (IW)	5
Car, toy	Colliding Cars (QL) Magnetic Poles (QL) Newton's Second Law (QL) What Changes Motion? (IW)	10
* Chair	Can You Feel the Power? (LI)	5
* Coins, various	Detecting Fake Coins (LI)	15
Comb, plastic	Drawing Conclusions (QL)	5
Compass, drawing	Magnetic Fields From Electric Current (QL)	5
Compass, magnetic	Electric Current and Magnetism (QL) Electromagnetism (IW) How Can Current Be Measured? (IW) Magnetic Fields From Electric Current (QL) Natural Magnets (IW) Spinning in Circles (QL)	5
* Corkscrew	Is It a Machine? (IW)	1
Cup, plastic	Electromagnet (QL)	5
Dowel, wood	Machines That Turn (IW)	5
Eddy demonstration	How are Electricity, Magnets, and Motion Related? (IW)	1
Flashlight	What Makes a Flashlight Shine? (IW)	5
* Freezer	Frosty Balloons (QL)	1
Funnel	Earth's Magnetic Field (QL) Thermal Properties (IW) What Is Work? (QL)	5
Galvanometer	Electric Current Without a Battery (IW) Inducing an Electric Current (QL)	5
Goggles	Temperature and Thermal Energy (QL) What Makes an Object Move in a Circle? (IW) What Would Make a Card Jump? (IW)	30

KEY:
* = School Supplied
Quantities based on five groups of six students per class.

Nonconsumables

Description	Activity Title	Quantity per Class
Graduated cylinder	Build Your Own Thermometer (LI)	5
Graphite rod	Calculating Electric Power and Energy Use (QL)	5
Hand generator	How Can You Make a Bulb Burn More Brightly? (IW) Sources of Energy (QL)	1
* Hole punch	Drawing Conclusions (QL)	1
* Hot plate	What Does It Mean to Heat Up? (IW)	5
* Household objects	Machines in the Kitchen (QL)	5
Light socket, miniature	Build a Flashlight (LI) Calculating Electric Power and Energy Use (QL) Conductors and Insulators (QL) Do the Lights Keep Shining? (IW) Electric Shock and Short Circuit Safety (QL) Electromagnetism (IW) How Can Current Be Measured? (IW) How Can You Make a Bulb Burn More Brightly? (IW) Ohm's Law (QL) Producing Electric Current (QL) Sources of Energy (QL)	15
Magnet, assorted bag	How Generators Work (QL)	1
Magnet, bar	Can a Magnet Move a Wire? (QL) Detecting Fake Coins (LI) Earth's Magnetic Field (QL) Inducing an Electric Current (QL) Magnetic Poles (QL) Natural Magnets (IW) Predict the Field (IW) Spinning in Circles (QL)	10
Magnet, bar (ceramic)	Magnetic Poles (QL)	5
Magnet, disk	How Galvanometers Work (QL) How Generators Work (QL) Parts of an Electric Motor (QL) Predict the Field (IW)	10
Magnet, horseshoe	Electric Current Without a Battery (IW) Predict the Field (IW)	5
Marble	Describing Acceleration (QL) How Pushy Is a Straw? (IW) Orbiting Earth (QL)	20
Masses, hooked	Angling for Access (LI) Building Pulleys (QL) Inclined Planes and Levers (IW) Sticky Sneakers (LI)	5
Metal rod	What Does It Mean to Heat Up? (IW)	5

KEY:
* = School Supplied
Quantities based on five groups of six students per class.

MASTER MATERIALS LIST (continued)

Nonconsumables

Description	Activity Title	Quantity per Class
Meter stick	Can You Feel the Power? (LI) Describing Acceleration (QL) Determining Mechanical Energy (QL) Graphing Acceleration (QL) How Fast and How Far? (IW) How High Does a Ball Bounce? (IW) Investigating Power (QL) Law of Conservation of Energy (QL) Mechanical Advantage (QL) Soaring Straws (QL) Stopping on a Dime (LI) Velocity (QL) What Is Motion? (IW) What Is Work? (QL)	10
Mineral, hematite	Natural Magnets (IW)	5
Mineral, lodestone	Natural Magnets (IW)	5
Mineral, magnetite	Natural Magnets (IW)	5
* Mug, coffee	Going Up (QL) Pulling at an Angle (IW)	5
Multimeter	Calculating Electric Power and Energy Use (QL)	1
Nails, package	Electromagnet (QL)	1
* Object, heavy	Observing Friction (IW)	5
Oven mitts	What Does It Mean to Heat Up? (IW)	5
* Paint can or barbell	Investigating Power (QL)	20
Pan or basin	Modeling Potential Difference (QL)	5
Paper clips, box	Electromagnet (QL)	1
Protractor	Detecting Fake Coins (LI) How Can Current Be Measured? (IW)	5
Pulley	Building Pulleys (QL)	5
Rope	Modeling Unbalanced Forces (QL)	1
Ruler, metric	Angling for Access (LI) Build Your Own Thermometer (LI) Calculating Electric Power and Energy Use (QL) Can a Magnet Move a Wire? (QL) Detecting Fake Coins (LI) Determining Mechanical Energy (QL) How Can Current Be Measured? (IW) Inclined Planes and Levers (IW) Mechanical Advantage (QL) Motion Graphs (QL) Soaring Straws (QL) Which Lands First? (QL)	5

KEY:
* = School Supplied
Quantities based on five groups of six students per class.

MASTER MATERIALS LIST (continued)

Nonconsumables

Description	Activity Title	Quantity per Class
* Scissors	Around and Around (QL) Build a Flashlight (LI) Calculating (QL) Earth's Magnetic Field (QL) How Galvanometers Work (QL) How Generators Work (QL) Interpreting Illustrations (QL) Is the Force With You? (IW) Orbiting Earth (QL) Soaring Straws (QL) Sparks Are Flying (QL) What Makes an Object Move in a Circle? (IW) What Would Make a Card Jump? (IW)	5
* Scissors with tension adjustment	Friction and Efficiency (QL)	5
* Screwdriver	Build a Flashlight (LI) Is It a Machine? (IW)	5
* Shoe	Calculating (QL)	5
* Shoe box	Determining Mechanical Energy (QL)	5
* Skateboard	Is the Force With You? (IW) Mass, Velocity, and Kinetic Energy (QL)	5
* Sneakers, three different types	Sticky Sneakers (LI)	15
Spool, empty	How Transformers Works (QL) What Makes an Object Move in a Circle? (IW)	10
Spring scale, 1-kg	Building Pulleys (QL) Investigating Power (QL) Is the Force With You? (IW)	10
Spring scale, 2-kg	Angling for Access (LI) Going Up (QL) Inclined Planes and Levers (IW) Sticky Sneakers (LI) What Is Force? (QL) What Is Work? (QL)	10
Spring scale, 500-g	Sticky Sneakers (LI)	5
Stopper	Machines That Turn (IW)	5
Switch, knife	Can a Magnet Move a Wire? (QL) Electromagnetism (IW)	5
Tape measure	Frosty Balloons (QL) Motion Graphs (QL) Stopping on a Dime (LI) Will You Hurry Up? (IW)	5
Test tube rack	Temperature and Thermal Energy (QL) Thermal Properties (IW) Visualizing Convection Currents (QL)	5
Test tubes, glass	Thermal Properties (IW) Visualizing Convection Currents (QL)	15
Test tubes, plastic	Earth's Magnetic Field (QL) Temperature and Thermal Energy (QL)	5

KEY:
* = School Supplied
Quantities based on five groups of six students per class.

Nonconsumables

	Description	Activity Title	Quantity per Class
	Thermometer	Build Your Own Thermometer (LI) Temperature and Thermal Energy (QL) Thermal Properties (IW)	15
*	Tile flooring	Sticky Sneakers (LI)	5
	Timer/ stopwatch	Can You Feel the Power? (LI) Describing Acceleration (QL) Graphing Acceleration (QL) How Are Electricity, Magnets, and Motion Related? (IW) How Fast and How Far? (IW) Investigating Power (QL) Motion Graphs (QL) Stopping on a Dime (LI) Temperature and Thermal Energy (QL) Velocity (QL) Will You Hurry Up? (IW)	10
	Tongs, beaker	Thermal Properties (IW)	5
	Tube, cardboard	Soaring Straws (QL)	5
	Tubing, vinyl foot	Modeling Potential Difference (QL)	6
	Vial	How Generators Work (QL)	5
	Washers, coin sized	Detecting Fake Coins (LI)	5
	Washers	Newton's Second Law (QL) What Changes Motion? (IW) What Is Force? (QL)	60
	Wire, aluminum	Conductors and Insulators (QL)	5
	Wire cutters	Build a Flashlight (LI) How Can Current Be Measured? (IW) Producing Electric Current (QL)	
	Wooden block	Angling for Access (LI)	5

KEY:
* = School Supplied
Quantities based on five groups of six students per class.

Consumables

	Description	Activity Titles	Quantity per Class
*	Aluminum can with tab	What Is Work? (QL)	5
	Aluminum foil, roll	Build a Flashlight (LI)	1
	Balloons	Can You Move a Can Without Touching It? (IW) Frosty Balloons (QL)	10
*	Batteries, D cell	Build a Flashlight (LI) Calculating Electric Power and Energy Use (QL) Conductors and Insulators (QL) Do the Lights Keep Shining? (IW) Electromagnet (QL) Electromagnetism (IW) How Can Current Be Measured? (IW) How Galvanometers Work (QL) Ohm's Law (QL) Parts of an Electric Motor (QL) Producing Electric Current (QL) What Makes a Flashlight Shine? (IW)	20
	Battery, 6V (dry cell)	Can a Magnet Move a Wire? (QL) Electric Current and Magnetism (QL) Electric Shock and Short Circuit Safety (QL) Magnetic Fields From Electric Current (QL) Sources of Energy (QL)	5
*	Bottle, soda 16 oz	Earth's Magnetic Field (QL) Modeling Potential Difference (QL)	5
*	Bottle, 1-L	Build Your Own Thermometer (LI)	5
*	Box, cardboard	Magnetic Fields From Electric Current (QL)	5
	Bulb, miniature	Build a Flashlight (LI) Calculating Electric Power and Energy Use (QL) Conductors and Insulators (QL) Do the Lights Keep Shining? (IW) Electric Shock and Short Circuit Safety (QL) Electromagnetism (IW) How Can Current Be Measured? (IW) How Can You Make a Bulb Burn More Brightly? (IW) Ohm's Law (QL) Producing Electric Current (QL) Sources of Energy (QL)	10
*	Butter, frozen	What Does It Mean to Heat Up? (IW)	5
*	Can, aluminum	Can You Move a Can Without Touching It? (IW)	5
	Cardboard, white	Detecting Fake Coins (LI)	5
	Chalk, box	Is It a Machine? (IW)	1
	Cloth	Thermal Properties (IW)	5
	Craft sticks	Detecting Fake Coins (LI)	5
	Cup, foam	Temperature and Thermal Energy (QL)	5
	Cup, paper	Build a Flashlight (LI)	5

KEY:
* = School Supplied
Quantities based on five groups of six students per class.

Consumables

	Description	Activity Titles	Quantity per Class
	Cup, paper small	How Transformers Work (QL)	15
	Dropper, plastic	Build Your Own Thermometer (LI) Visualizing Convection Currents (QL)	5
	Food coloring, blue bottle	Visualizing Convection Currents (QL)	1
	Food coloring, red bottle	Build Your Own Thermometer (LI) Visualizing Convection Currents (QL)	1
*	Glue, bottle	Interpreting Illustrations (QL)	5
	Gravel, bag	What Is Work? (QL)	1
	Index cards, pack	What Would Make a Card Jump? (IW)	1
	Iron filings, bottle	Earth's Magnetic Field (QL) Predict the Field (IW)	1
	LED, bulb	How Generators Work (QL)	5
	Lid, foam cup	Temperature and Thermal Energy (QL)	5
*	Magazines	Interpreting Illustrations (QL)	20
*	Markers	Angling for Access (LI) Build Your Own Thermometer (LI) Describing Acceleration (QL) Frosty Balloons (QL) How Cold Is the Water? (IW) How Transformers Work (QL) Inclined Planes and Levers (IW) Soaring Straws (QL) What Is Motion? (IW)	5
*	Marker, permanent	Interpreting Illustrations (QL)	5
	Modeling clay, package	Build Your Own Thermometer (LI) Determining Mechanical Energy (QL) Electric Current Without a Battery (IW) How Can Current Be Measured? (IW) How Transformers Work (QL) Modeling Potential Difference (QL) Parts of an Electric Motor (QL)	2
*	Newspapers	Mechanical Advantage (QL)	15
*	Notebook, spiral	Calculating (QL)	5
	Pan, round	Sparks Are Flying (QL)	5
	Paper clips, jumbo	Newton's Second Law (QL) Parts of an Electric Motor (QL) Sticky Sneakers (LI) Thermal Properties (IW)	30
*	Paper, graph	Graphing Acceleration (QL) Motion Graphs (QL) Soaring Straws (QL) Temperature and Thermal Energy (QL)	5
*	Paper, notebook	Observing Friction (IW)	10
	Paper, tissue	Drawing Conclusions (QL)	5

KEY:
* = School Supplied
Quantities based on five groups of six students per class.

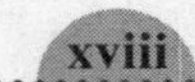

Consumables

	Description	Activity Titles	Quantity per Class
*	Paper, white	Calculating Electric Power and Energy Use (QL) Friction and Efficiency (QL) How Cold Is the Water? (IW) Is It a Machine? (IW) Spinning in Circles (QL)	5
*	Pencils	Can a Magnet Move a Wire? (QL) Detecting Fake Coins (LI) Going Up (QL) Inclined Planes and Levers (IW) Is It a Machine? (IW) Motion Graphs (QL) Spinning in Circles (QL)	5
*	Pencil with lead showing	Ohm's Law (QL)	5
	Petri dish	Predict the Field (IW)	5
	Plate, foam	Sparks Are Flying (QL)	10
*	Pliers	Is It a Machine? (IW) Parts of an Electric Motor (QL)	5
*	Posterboard	Interpreting Illustrations (QL)	5
	Pulley cord	Building Pulleys (QL)	5
*	Quarters	Which Lands First? (QL)	20
	Rod, acrylic	What Does It Mean to Heat Up? (IW)	5
	Rod, glass	What Does It Mean to Heat Up? (IW)	5
	Rubber band	Conductors and Insulators (QL) Detecting Fake Coins (LI) How Pushy Is a Straw? (IW) Pulling at an Angle (IW) Soaring Straws (QL) Thermal Properties (IW) What Would Make a Card Jump? (IW)	10
	Sandpaper, sheet	How Galvanometers Work (QL) Observing Friction (IW) Parts of an Electric Motor (QL) Sticky Sneakers (LI)	5
	Seed, beans, bag	Modeling Levers (QL)	1
	Spoon, plastic	Modeling Levers (QL) Visualizing Convection Currents (QL)	5
	Steel wool pad	Electric Shock and Short Circuit Safety (QL)	1
	Stirrer stick	How Galvanometers Work (QL)	5
	Straws	Build Your Own Thermometer (LI) Detecting Fake Coins (LI) How Galvanometers Work (QL) How Pushy Is a Straw? (IW) How Transformers Work (QL) Soaring Straws (QL)	10

KEY:
* = School Supplied
Quantities based on five groups of six students per class.

Consumables

Description	Activity Titles	Quantity per Class
String, roll	Around and Around (QL) Conductors and Insulators (QL) Earth's Magnetic Field (QL) Going Up (QL) How Transformers Work (QL) Inclined Planes and Levers (IW) Is the Force With You? (IW) Newton's Second Law (QL) What Is Work? (QL) What Makes an Object Move in a Circle? (IW)	1
Tag board, sheet	Orbiting Earth (QL)	5
* Tape, clear	How Generators Work (QL)	1
Tape, duct	Build a Flashlight (LI)	1
Tape, electrical	Electromagnet (QL) How Can Current Be Measured? (IW)	1
Tape, masking roll	Around and Around (QL) Colliding Cars (QL) Describing Acceleration (QL) Detecting Fake Coins (LI) Electric Current and Magnetism (QL) Graphing Acceleration (QL) How Fast and How Far? (IW) How Transformers Work (QL) Inclined Planes and Levers (IW) Magnetic Poles (QL) Modeling Unbalanced Forces (QL) Motion Graphs (QL) Newton's Second Law (QL) Orbiting Earth (QL) Soaring Straws (QL) Sparks Are Flying (QL) Sticky Sneakers (LI) Velocity (QL) What Is Motion? (IW) What Is Work? (QL) Which Lands First? (QL) Will You Hurry Up? (IW)	1
Tongue depressor	Detecting Fake Coins (LI)	5
Tube, cardboard	Build a Flashlight (LI)	5
Vegetable oil, bottle	Build Your Own Thermometer (LI)	1
Water, cold	How Cold Is the Water? (IW) Temperature and Thermal Energy (QL) Visualizing Convection Currents (QL)	
Water, hot	Build Your Own Thermometer (LI) How Cold Is the Water? (IW) Temperature and Thermal Energy (QL) Thermal Properties (IW) Visualizing Convection Currents (QL) What Does It Mean to Heat Up? (IW)	

KEY:
* = School Supplied
Quantities based on five groups of six students per class.

Consumables

Description	Activity Titles	Quantity per Class
Water, ice	Build Your Own Thermometer (LI)	
Water, tap	Build Your Own Thermometer (LI) How Cold Is the Water? (IW) Pulling at an Angle (IW)	
Wax paper, roll	Observing Friction (IW)	1
Wire, bell roll	Conductors and Insulators (QL) How Can Current Be Measured? (IW) Producing Electric Current (QL)	1
Wire, bare copper	Conductors and Insulators (QL)	1
Wire, enameled (magnet) roll	Can a Magnet Move a Wire? (QL) How Galvanometers Work (QL) How Generators Work (QL) Inducing an Electric Current (QL) Parts of an Electric Motor (QL)	1
Wire, insulated roll	Build a Flashlight (LI) Can a Magnet Move a Wire? (QL) Do the Lights Keep Shining? (IW) Electric Current Without a Battery (IW) Electric Current and Magnetism (QL) Electromagnet (QL) Electomagnetism (IW) How Can You Make a Bulb Burn More Brightly? (IW) Magnetic Fields From Electric Current (QL)	1

KEY:
* = School Supplied
Quantities based on five groups of six students per class.

To prepare yourself to work safely in the laboratory, read the following safety rules. Then read them a second time. Make sure you understand and follow each rule. Ask your teacher to explain any rules you do not understand.

Dress Code

1. To protect yourself from injuring your eyes, wear safety goggles whenever you work with chemicals, glassware, heat sources such as burners, or any substance that might get into your eyes. If you wear contact lenses, notify your teacher.
2. Wear a lab apron or coat whenever you work with corrosive chemicals or substances that can stain.
3. Remove or tie back any article of clothing or jewelry that can hang down and touch chemicals, flames, or equipment. Roll up or secure long sleeves. Never wear open shoes or sandals.

General Precautions

4. Read all directions for an experiment several times before beginning the activity. Carefully follow all written and oral instructions. If you are in doubt about any part of the experiment, ask your teacher for assistance.
5. Never perform activities that are not assigned or authorized by your teacher. Never handle any equipment unless you have specific permission.
6. Never eat or drink in the laboratory.
7. Keep work areas clean and uncluttered. Bring only notebooks, lab manuals, or written lab procedures to the work area. All other items should be left in a designated area.
8. Do not engage in horseplay.

First Aid

9. Report all accidents, injuries, or fires to your teacher, no matter how minor.
10. Learn what to do in cases of specific accidents, such as getting acid in your eyes or on your skin. (Rinse acids from your body with plenty of water.)
11. Be aware of the location of the first-aid kit, but do not use it unless instructed by your teacher. In case of injury, your teacher should administer first aid. Your teacher may also send you to the school nurse or call a physician.
12. Know the location of the emergency equipment such as the fire extinguisher and fire blanket.
13. Know the location of the nearest telephone and whom to contact in an emergency.

Heating and Fire Safety

14. Never use a heat source, such as a candle, burner, or hot plate, without wearing safety goggles.
15. Never heat anything unless instructed to do so. A chemical that is harmless when cool may be dangerous when heated.
16. Never use a flame or spark near a combustible chemical or material.
17. Never reach across a flame.
18. Before using a laboratory burner, make sure you know proper procedures for lighting and adjusting the burner, as demonstrated by your teacher. Do not touch the burner. It may be hot. Never leave a lighted burner unattended. Turn off the burner when it is not in use.
19. Chemicals can splash or boil out of a heated test tube. When heating a substance in a test tube, make sure that the mouth of the tube is not pointed at you or anyone else.
20. Never heat a liquid in a closed container. The expanding gases produced may shatter the container.
21. Before picking up a container that has been heated, first hold the back of your hand near it. If you can feel heat on the back of your hand, the container is too hot to handle. Use an oven mitt to pick up a container that has been heated.

Using Chemicals Safely

22. Never mix chemicals "for the fun of it." You might produce a dangerous, possibly explosive substance.
23. Never put your face near the mouth of a container that holds chemicals. Many chemicals are poisonous. Never touch, taste, or smell a chemical unless you are instructed to do so by your teacher.
24. Use only those chemicals needed in the activity. Read and double-check labels on supply bottles before removing any chemicals. Take only as much as you need. Keep all containers closed when chemicals are not being used.
25. Dispose of excess chemicals as instructed by your teacher. To avoid contamination, never return chemicals to their original containers. Never pour untreated chemicals or other substances into the sink or trash containers.
26. Be extra careful when working with acids or bases. Take extreme care not to spill any material in the laboratory. Wash chemical spills and splashes immediately with plenty of water. Immediately begin rinsing with water any acids that get on your skin or clothing, and notify your teacher of any acid spill.
27. If you are instructed to test for odors, use a wafting motion to direct the odors to your nose. Do not inhale the fumes directly from the container.
28. When mixing an acid and water, always pour the water into the container first and then add the acid to the water. Never pour water into an acid.

Using Glassware Safely

29. Never force glass tubing or thermometers into a rubber stopper or rubber tubing. Have your teacher insert the glass tubing or thermometer if required for an activity.
30. If you are using a laboratory burner, use a wire screen to protect glassware from any flame. Never heat glassware that is not thoroughly dry on the outside.
31. Keep in mind that hot glassware looks cool. Never pick up glassware without first checking to see if it is hot. Use an oven mitt. See rule 21.
32. Never use broken or chipped glassware. If glassware is broken or chipped, notify your teacher and dispose of the glassware in the proper container.
33. Never eat or drink from glassware.
34. Thoroughly clean glassware before putting it away.

Using Sharp Instruments

35. Handle scalpels or other sharp instruments with extreme care. Never cut material toward you; cut away from you.
36. Immediately notify your teacher if you cut your skin when working in the laboratory.

Animal and Plant Safety

37. Never perform experiments that cause pain, discomfort, or harm to animals. This rule applies at home as well as in the classroom.
38. Only handle animals if absolutely necessary. Your teacher will instruct you how to handle each animal species brought into the classroom.
39. If you are allergic to certain plants, molds, or animals, tell your teacher before doing an activity in which these are used.
40. During field work, wear long pants, long sleeves, socks, and closed shoes. Avoid poisonous plants and fungi as well as plants with thorns. Never eat any part of a plant or fungus.
41. Wash your hands thoroughly after any activity involving animals, animal parts, plants, plant parts, or soil.

End-of-Experiment Rules

42. After an experiment has been completed, turn off all burners and unplug all electrical equipment. If you used a gas burner, check that the gas-line valve to the burner is off. Unplug hot plates.
43. Clean up your work area and return all equipment to its proper place.
44. Dispose of waste materials as instructed by you teacher.
45. Wash your hands after every experiment.

These symbols warn of possible dangers in the laboratory and remind you to work carefully.

Safety Goggles Wear safety goggles to protect your eyes in any activity involving chemicals, flames or heating, or glassware.

Lab Apron Wear a laboratory apron to protect your skin and clothing from damage.

Breakage Handle breakable materials, such as glassware, with care. Do not touch broken glassware.

Heat-Resistant Gloves Use an oven mitt or other hand protection when handling hot materials, such as hot plates or hot glassware.

Plastic Gloves Wear disposable plastic gloves when working with harmful chemicals and organisms. Keep your hands away from your face, and dispose of the gloves according to your teacher's instructions.

Heating Use a clamp or tongs to pick up hot glassware. Do not touch hot objects with your bare hands.

Flames Before you work with flames, tie back loose hair and clothing. Follow instructions from your teacher about lighting and extinguishing flames.

No Flames When using flammable materials, make sure there are no flames, sparks, or other exposed heat sources present.

Corrosive Chemical Avoid getting acid or other corrosive chemicals on your skin or clothing or in your eyes. Do not inhale the vapors. Wash your hands after the activity.

Poison Do not let any poisonous chemical come into contact with your skin, and do not inhale its vapors. Wash your hands when you are finished with the activity.

Fumes Work in a well-ventilated area when harmful vapors may be involved. Avoid inhaling vapors directly. Only test an odor when directed to do so by your teacher, and use a wafting motion to direct the vapor toward your nose.

Sharp Object Scissors, scalpels, knives, needles, pins, and tacks can cut your skin. Always direct a sharp edge or point away from yourself and others.

Animal Safety Treat live or preserved animals or animal parts with care to avoid harming the animals or yourself. Wash your hands when you are finished with the activity.

Plant Safety Handle plants only as directed by your teacher. If you are allergic to certain plants, tell your teacher; do not do an activity involving those plants. Avoid touching harmful plants such as poison ivy. Wash your hands when you are finished with the activity.

Electric Shock To avoid electric shock, never use electrical equipment around water, or when the equipment is wet or your hands are wet. Be sure cords are untangled and cannot trip anyone. Unplug equipment not in use.

Physical Safety When an experiment involves physical activity, avoid injuring yourself or others. Alert your teacher if there is any reason you should not participate.

Disposal Dispose of chemicals and other laboratory materials safely. Follow the instructions from your teacher.

Hand Washing Wash your hands thoroughly when finished with an activity. Use soap and warm water. Rinse well.

General Safety Awareness When this symbol appears, follow the instructions provided. When you are asked to develop your own procedure in a lab, have your teacher approve your plan before you go further.

Name ______________________ Date ____________ Class ____________

Laboratory Safety Contract

I, ____,

(please print full name)

have read the Science Safety Rules and Safety Symbols sections, understand their contents completely, and agree to demonstrate compliance with all safety rules and guidelines that have been established in each of the following categories:

(please check)

- ❒ Dress Code
- ❒ General Precautions
- ❒ First Aid
- ❒ Heating and Fire Safety
- ❒ Using Chemicals Safely
- ❒ Using Glassware Safely
- ❒ Using Sharp Instruments
- ❒ Animal and Plant Safety
- ❒ End-of-Experiment Rules

____

(signature)

Date ____

Name ______________________ Date ____________ Class ____________

Student Safety Test: Recognizing Laboratory Safety

Pre-Lab Discussion

An important part of your study of science will be working in a laboratory. In the laboratory, you and your classmates will learn about the natural world by conducting experiments. Working directly with household objects, laboratory equipment, and even living things will help you to better understand the concepts you read about in your textbook or in class.

Most of the laboratory work you will do is quite safe. However, some laboratory equipment, chemicals, and specimens can be dangerous if handled improperly. Laboratory accidents do not just happen. They are caused by carelessness, improper handling of equipment, or inappropriate behavior.

In this investigation, you will learn how to prevent accidents and thus work safely in a laboratory. You will review some safety guidelines and become acquainted with the location and proper use of safety equipment in your classroom laboratory.

Problem

What are the proper practices for working safely in a science laboratory?

Materials (per group)

Science textbook
Laboratory safety equipment (for demonstration)

Procedure

Part 1. Reviewing Laboratory Safety Rules and Symbols

1. Carefully read the list of laboratory safety rules listed on pages xxii and xxiii of this lab resource.

2. Special symbols are used throughout this resource to call attention to investigations that require extra caution. Use pages xxiv and xxv as a reference to describe what each symbol means in numbers 1 through 8 in Part 1 under Observations.

Part 2. Location of Safety Equipment in Your Science Laboratory

1. The teacher will point out the location of the safety equipment in your classroom laboratory. Pay special attention to instructions for using such equipment as fire extinguishers, eyewash fountains, fire blankets, safety showers, and items in first-aid kits. Use the space provided in Part 2 under Observations to list the location of all safety equipment in your laboratory.

Name________________________ Date______________ Class______________

Recognizing Laboratory Safety (continued)

Observations

Part 1

 **1.** ____

 **2.** ____

3. ____

4. ____

5. ____

 **6.** ____

 **7.** ____

8. ____

Name ______________________________ Date ______________ Class ______________

Recognizing Laboratory Safety (continued)

Observations

Part 2

____

____

____

____

Analyze and Conclude

Look at each of the following drawings and explain why the laboratory activities pictured are unsafe.

1. ____

____

____

____

2. ____

____

____

____

3. ____

____

____

____

Name ______________________________ Date______________ Class______________

Recognizing Laboratory Safety (continued)

Critical Thinking and Applications

In each of the following situations, write *yes* if the proper safety procedures are being followed and *no* if they are not. Then give a reason for your answer.

1. Gina is thirsty. She rinses a beaker with water, refills it with water, and takes a drink.

____

____

2. Bram noticed that the electrical cord on his microscope is frayed near the plug. He takes the microscope to his teacher and asks for permission to use another one.

____

____

3. The printed directions in the lab book tell a student to pour a small amount of hydrochloric acid into a beaker. Jamal puts on safety goggles before pouring the acid into the beaker.

____

____

4. It is rather warm in the laboratory during a late spring day. Anna slips off her shoes and walks barefoot to the sink to clean her glassware.

____

____

5. While washing glassware, Mike splashes some water on Evon. To get even, Evon splashes him back.

____

____

6. During an experiment, Lindsey decides to mix two chemicals that the lab procedure does not say to mix, because she is curious about what will happen.

____

____

Name ______________________ Date __________ Class __________

Laboratory Skills Checkup 1

Following Directions

1. Read all of the following directions before you do anything.
2. Print your name, last name first, then your first name and middle initial (if you have one), at the top of this page.
3. Draw a line through the word "all" in direction 1.
4. Underline the word "directions" in direction 1.
5. In direction 2, circle the words "your first name."
6. In direction 3, place an "X" in front of the word "through."
7. Cross out the numbers of the even-numbered directions above.
8. In direction 7, cross out the word "above" and write the word "below" above it.
9. Write "Following directions is easy" under your name at the top of this page.
10. In direction 9, add the following sentence after the word "page": "That's what you think!"
11. Draw a square in the upper right corner of this page.
12. Draw a triangle in the lower left corner of this page.
13. Place a circle in the center of the square.
14. Place an "X" in the center of the triangle.
15. Now that you have read all the directions as instructed in direction 1, follow directions 2 and 16 only.
16. Please do not give away what this test is about by saying anything or doing anything to alert your classmates. If you have reached this direction, make believe you are still writing. See how many of your classmates really know how to follow directions.

Name ______________________ Date ______________ Class ______________

Laboratory Skills Checkup 2

Defining Elements of Scientific Inquiry

Laboratory activities and experiments involve the process of scientific inquiry. Listed in the left column are the names of parts of this method. The right column contains definitions. Next to each word in the left column, write the letter of the definition that best matches that word.

_____ **1.** Hypothesis

_____ **2.** Manipulated Variable

_____ **3.** Responding Variable

_____ **4.** Controlling Variables

_____ **5.** Observation

_____ **6.** Data

_____ **7.** Conclusion

A. Prediction about the outcome of an experiment

B. What you measure or observe to obtain your results

C. Measurements and other observations

D. Statement that sums up what you learn from an experiment

E. Factor that is changed in an experiment

F. What the person performing the activity sees, hears, feels, smells, or tastes

G. Keeping all variables the same except the manipulated variable

Name ______________________ Date__________ Class__________

Laboratory Skills Checkup 3

Analyzing Elements of Scientific Inquiry

Read the following statements and then answer the questions.

1. You and your friend are walking along a beach in Maine on January 15, at 8:00 A.M.
2. You notice a thermometer on a nearby building that reads –1°C.
3. You also notice that there is snow on the roof of the building and icicles hanging from the roof.
4. You further notice a pool of seawater in the sand near the ocean.
5. Your friend looks at the icicles and the pool and says, "Why is the water on the roof frozen and the seawater is not?"
6. You answer, "I think that the salt in the seawater keeps it from freezing at –1°C."
7. You go on to say, "And I think under the same conditions, the same thing will happen tomorrow."
8. Your friend asks, "How can you be sure?" You answer, "I'm going to get some fresh water and some salt water and expose them to a temperature of –1°C and see what happens."

Questions

A. In which statement is a **prediction** made? __________

B. Which statement identifies a **problem**? __________

C. In which statement is an **experiment** described? __________

D. Which statement contains a **hypothesis**? __________

E. Which statements contain **data**? __________

F. Which statements describe **observations**? __________

Name ______________________ Date______________ Class______________

Laboratory Skills Checkup 4

Performing an Experiment

Read the following statements and then answer the questions.

1. A scientist wants to find out why seawater freezes at a lower temperature than fresh water.
2. The scientist goes to the library and reads a number of articles about the physical properties of solutions.
3. The scientist also reads about the composition of seawater.
4. The scientist travels to a nearby beach and observes the conditions there. The scientist notes the taste of the seawater and other factors such as waves, wind, air pressure, temperature, and humidity.
5. After considering all this information, the scientist sits at a desk and writes, "If seawater has salt in it, it will freeze at a lower temperature than fresh water."
6. The scientist goes back to the laboratory and does the following:
   a. Fills each of two beakers with 1 liter of fresh water.
   b. Dissolves 35 grams of table salt in one of the beakers.
   c. Places both beakers in a freezer at a temperature of −1°C.
   d. Leaves the beakers in the freezer for 24 hours.
7. After 24 hours, the scientist examines both beakers and finds the fresh water to be frozen. The salt water is still liquid.
8. The scientist writes in a notebook, "It appears that salt water freezes at a lower temperature than fresh water does."
9. The scientist continues, "I suggest that the reason seawater freezes at a lower temperature is that seawater contains dissolved salts, while fresh water does not."

Questions

A. Which statement(s) contain **conclusions**? ____________

B. Which statement(s) contain a **hypothesis**? ____________

C. Which statement(s) contain **observations**? ____________

D. Which statement(s) describe an **experiment**? ____________

E. In which statement is the **problem** described? ____________

F. Which statement(s) contain **data**? ____________

G. What is the **manipulated variable** in the experiment? ____________

H. What is the **responding variable** in the experiment? ____________

Name ______________________ Date ____________ Class ____________

Laboratory Skills Checkup 5

Identifying Errors

Read the following paragraph and then answer the questions.

Andrew arrived at school and went directly to his Earth science class. He took off his cap and coat and sat down at his desk. His teacher gave him a large rock and asked him to find its density. Realizing that the rock was too large to work with, Andrew got a hammer from the supply cabinet and hit the rock several times until he broke off a chip small enough to work with. He partly filled a graduated cylinder with water and suspended the rock in the water. The water level rose 2 cm. Andrew committed this measurement to memory. He next weighed the rock on a balance. The rock weighed 4 oz. Andrew then calculated the density of the rock as follows: He divided 2 cm by 4 oz. He then reported to his teacher that the density of the rock was .5 cm/oz.

Questions

1. What safety rule(s) did Andrew break? ______________________

2. What mistake did Andrew make using measurement units?

3. What should Andrew have done with his data rather than commit them to memory?

4. What is wrong with the statement, "He next weighed the rock on a balance"?

5. Why is "4 oz" an inappropriate measurement in a science experiment?

6. What mistake did Andrew make in calculating density?

CHAPTER 1

TABLE OF CONTENTS

Motion

Teacher Notes 2

Describing Motion

Inquiry Warm-Up What Is Motion? 9

Quick Lab Identifying Motion 10

Speed and Velocity

Inquiry Warm-Up How Fast and How Far? 11

Lab Investigation Stopping on a Dime
- *Pre Lab* 12
- *Directed Inquiry* 13
- *Open Inquiry* 17

Quick Lab Velocity 21

Quick Lab Motion Graphs 22

Acceleration

Inquiry Warm-Up Will You Hurry Up? 23

Quick Lab Describing Acceleration 24

Quick Lab Graphing Acceleration 25

Describing Motion

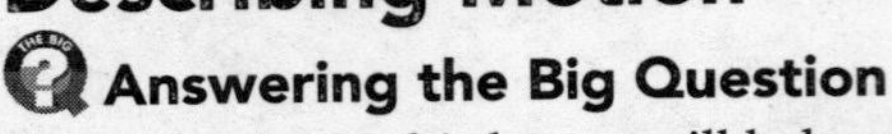

Answering the Big Question

The activities in this lesson will help students answer the Big Question by viewing and measuring the motion of objects. Students will identify relative motion and describe the varied ways that an object can move.

Inquiry Warm-Up

What Is Motion?

Inquiry Focus

Draw Conclusions—inferring by observation if an object moved relative to differing reference points

Group Size Groups

Class Time 15 minutes

Advance Preparation

1. A day ahead of time, ask students to bring in toys that may work in this activity. Emphasize that the toys must be relatively small and must not move too fast.
2. Butcher wrapping paper or parchment paper may be used. You can also cut standard sheets of paper lengthwise and tape them together. The paper should be at least 30 cm wide.

Alternative Materials

Unperforated, industrial-type rolls of paper towels or any other type of rolled paper will work well in this lab.

Procedure Tips

1. The toy should be able to move forward in a straight line but not too fast. A physics teacher may have devices called constant-motion cars.
2. If needed, adjust the distance between the start and finish lines to account for the speed of the toy.
3. The paper must be at least 2 m long in order to get the best results.

Answers

1. Yes, the toy was in motion. It moved from one position to another.
2. There were two reference points. The starting line marked on the paper and the piece of tape on the floor. The finish line can also be a reference point.
3. Sample Answer: The toy was in motion relative to the paper. It moved from the starting line to the finish line. However, the toy did not move relative to the floor.

Quick Lab

Identifying Motion

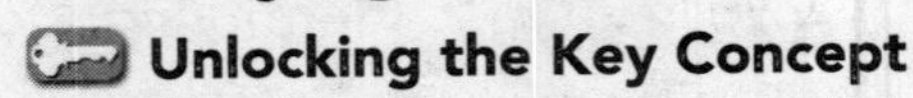

Unlocking the Key Concept

This activity will help students understand the concept of motion as the change in position of an object relative to a reference point.

Inquiry Focus

Observe—using the senses to gather information, in this case about the motion of a ball thrown from a stationary reference point and then from a moving reference point

Group Size Groups

Class Time 10 minutes

Safety

1. Be sure students remove any items from desks and tabletops that might be knocked off and damaged.
2. Instruct students to toss the ball only vertically.

Procedure Tips

1. Have students practice tossing the ball straight up from about chest level. Explain that the lower they release and catch the ball, the better view everyone will have of the ball's trajectory.
2. If time permits, rotate the job of tossing the ball through the group.
3. Provide ample space to walk. Students should be able to toss the ball a minimum of 4 times in order to observe good results. Students should also walk slowly.
4. Point out to students that the ball still has the forward motion of the person walking when it is tossed into the air.

Answers

1. Sample Answer: Everyone's observations were the same. The ball went up vertically and then came back down in the same vertical path.
2. Look for answers that show an understanding of reference point and motion. In general, the motion of the ball should appear to go up and down to the person tossing the ball. The group viewing should see the motion as series of arcs as the ball travels both up and down, and forward at the same time. The main reference point for the person tossing the ball is the person's hand, which seems stationary to that person. For the observing group, the reference points are the starting point of the walk and the level of the hand tossing the ball.

Speed and Velocity

Answering the Big Question

The activities in this lesson will help students answer the Big Question by having them observe motion, both qualitatively and qualitatively, and describing it in terms of speed and velocity and by graphing distance versus time.

Inquiry Warm-Up

How Fast and How Far?

Inquiry Focus

Form an Operational Definition—creating a working definition of speed by measuring the distance a student walks in a measured amount of time and expressing the result as speed

Group Size Pairs or groups

Class Time 15 minutes

Alternative Materials

A steel tape measure can be used instead of a meter stick.

Procedure Tips

1. Ideally, students should begin their walk well behind the first tape and continue beyond the second tape. In this way, students can observe and calculate a realistic walking speed without stopping and starting.
2. The student with the stopwatch should be in a position to see when the walker crosses both tapes, starting and stopping the watch accordingly. If this isn't practical, the walking student could carry the stopwatch while watching his or her steps.
3. When the student walks for five seconds, the first tape can be used as a marker to start timing. Another student should be ready with a piece of tape to stick at the distance walked at the end of 5 seconds.

Answers

1. Sample Answer: If I walk 5.0 m in 4.5 s, the speed equals (5.0 m/4.45 s) = 1.12 m/s. Walking an unspecified distance for 5.0 s should yield approximately the same speed.
2. Calculated speeds for trials 2 and 3 should have lower and higher values, respectively, than those in Step 2.
3. Look for answers that indicate an understanding of the idea that speed is equal to distance per unit time.

Lab Investigation

Stopping on a Dime

Unlocking the Key Concept

Both Versions This activity will help students understand that speed is the distance a moving object travels per unit of time. It also will allow students to design part of a basketball court based on their measurement of reaction times, running speeds, and stopping distances.

Answers—Pre Lab

Both Versions:

1. reaction time
2. You need to know how long it takes to stop from a full-speed run.
3. You need to know the distance covered and the time required to cover the distance.

Answers—Do the Math

$$\text{Average speed} = \frac{\text{Distance}}{\text{Time}} = \frac{25\text{m}}{8.6\text{ s}} = 2.9\text{ m/s}$$

Inquiry Focus

Directed Inquiry:

Calculate—using equations and mathematical processes to determine average speed

Interpret Data—analyzing and drawing conclusions from data in tabular form, looking for the extremes of reaction times, running times, and stopping distance and using this data to predict what would be a safe distance between the out-of-bounds line and the wall of a gym

Open Inquiry:

Calculate—determining the distance it could take basketball players to stop from a full sprint

Draw Conclusions—explaining why the slowest reaction time, the fastest sprint speed, and the longest stopping time must be used to determine the maximum potential stopping distance for a basketball player

Group Size

Directed Inquiry Pairs or groups

Open Inquiry Groups

Class Time

Both Versions 40 minutes

Advance Preparation (15 minutes)

Both Versions:

1. A day ahead, ask students to be sure to wear running shoes or other rubber-soled shoes.
2. Reserve time and space on the school athletic field or in the gymnasium for the second part of the lab.

Safety

1. Instruct students to run in the same direction as other students.
2. Review the Laboratory Safety Rules at the front of this book.
3. Students should wear safety goggles during the part of the lab in which reaction time is tested.

Alternative Materials

Both Versions:

If you do not have a metric tape measure, have students multiply feet by 0.305 to arrive at meters. A distance of 25 m is 82 feet.

Procedure Tips

Directed Inquiry:

1. Collect all groups' data, average them, and discuss them as a class.
2. Show students where running speed and stopping distance will be measured. Show where the timer will be placed and where the runner will begin and the direction the runner will travel.
3. Perform a sample calculation on the board.
4. Before students analyze their data, go through the logic used in arriving at the distance in Analyze and Conclude Question 3.
5. Expected Outcome: Typical reactions time is about 0.2 s. A typical running speed is about 5 m/s. A typical stopping distance is about 3 m. The safety margin should be about 4 m.
6. Be sure that the person dropping the meter stick does not inadvertently signal the person catching it.
7. Make sure students do not slow down before reaching the 25-m mark.

Open Inquiry:

1. Collect all groups' data, average them, and discuss them as a class.
2. Introduce the procedure by telling students that three things determine how far past the out-of-bounds line a player will travel: maximum running speed, reaction time, and stopping distance. Tell students where you will be going to measure running speed and stopping distance.
3. Make sure that the person dropping the meter stick does not inadvertently signal the person catching it.
4. Data tables should include columns for each group member's name, the distance the meter stick fell, and his or her reaction time. A typical reaction time is about 0.2 s.
5. Check over students' proposed experimental procedures and data tables. Refer to the direct inquiry version of this lab for one possible procedure. The table should include columns for each group member's name, maximum running speed, and stopping distance. A typical running speed is about 5 m/s. A typical stopping distance is about 3 m.

Answers—Analyze and Conclude

Directed Inquiry:

1. Students should find the student with the lowest time for running the course. Divide the 25-m distance by their time to get the maximum running speed in m/s. For example, 5 m/s.
2. This calculation combines the fastest student with the slowest reaction time. In that way, multiplying the maximum running speed by the slowest reaction time gives the maximum distance any runner might move before realizing that he or she needed to stop.
3. Assuming the student in Question 2 also has the longest measured stopping distance, the total distance calculated here represents how far he or she would travel out of bounds before coming to a complete stop.
4. Sample Answer: This answer represents the maximum distance it should take a student to stop, the so-called "worst-case scenario." It's highly unlikely that any one student will combine the fastest speed, the slowest reaction time, and the greatest stopping distance. In other words, all students should be able to stop in a distance that is shorter than the one calculated.
5. Sample Answer: A player might go out of bounds running sideways, jumping, or stumbling. A player might not immediately realize that he or she is out of bounds. These factors might increase the distance the player travels out of bounds.

Open Inquiry:

1. Find the student with the lowest time for running the course. Divide the distance in meters by their time to get the maximum running speed in m/s. Sample answer: The average speed of the fastest member of the group was 5.3 m/s.
2. Sample Answer: 1.9 m (equation: $5.3 \text{ m/s} \times .35\text{s} = 1.85 \text{ m}$). Multiplying the maximum running speed by the slowest reaction time gives the maximum out-of-bounds distance possible before any student in the group would realize that he or she needed to stop.
3. Sample Answer: 4.5 m (equation: $1.9 \text{ m} + 2.6 \text{ m} = 4.5 \text{ m}$). Assuming the student in Question 2 also has the longest measured stopping distance, the total distance calculated here represents how far he or she would travel out of bounds before coming to a complete stop. It is also the minimum safe distance between the out-of-bounds line and the wall.
4. Sample Answer: This answer represents the maximum distance it should take a student to stop. Because it is unlikely that any one student will combine the fastest speed, the slowest reaction time, and the greatest stopping distance all students should be able to stop in a distance that is shorter than the one calculated.

Answers—Post Lab

Directed Inquiry:

1. The experiment would have to include a measure of reaction time while running across a line. A radar speed-measuring device might be required in order to determine when the runner begins to slow down. Students might also suggest using a video camera that shows time. The result would have to be examined frame by frame.
2. Sample Answer: Students should mention speed and reaction time and probably will add the kind of shoe soles, the composition of the floor, and whether the floor is damp or dry.
3. Students should indicate that they calculated the maximum stopping distance between the line and the wall. They may want to find out what is done in real gyms to account for this safety problem.

Communicate—Students' proposals might consider additional, more visible markings, an audible alarm, and plenty of padding on the gym walls.

Open Inquiry:

1. Sample Answer: Potential variables included the distance run and the running surface. We all ran the same distance on the same surface.
2. Sample Answer: A player might go out of bounds running sideways, jumping, or stumbling. A player might not immediately realize that he or she is out of bounds. These factors might increase the distance the player travels out of bounds.

3. Sample Answer: Reaction times and stopping time might be used in designing traffic intersections, bike lanes, and other settings in which collisions might take place.
4. Students should indicate that they calculated the maximum stopping distance between the line and the wall. They may want to find out what is done in real gyms to account for this safety problem.

Communicate—Look for proposals that clearly describes the problem and, perhaps, gives examples of students who have been injured. Students should be sure to include measurements and calculations in their proposals. Be sure students understand that moving a wall to gain more out-of-bounds room probably isn't practical, so their solutions should concentrate on making the in-bounds portion of the court smaller.

Quick Lab

Velocity

Unlocking the Key Concept

This activity will help students understand the concept of velocity as speed in a given direction and will help them differentiate velocity from speed.

Inquiry Focus

Form an Operational Definition—creating a working definition, in this case of velocity, contrasting it with speed

Group Size Groups

Class Time 15 minutes

Advance Preparation (5 minutes)

1. A day ahead, ask students to bring in toys that may work in this activity. Emphasize that the toys must be relatively small and must not move too fast. Battery-powered toys may be used if they meet all other criteria.
2. Distribute tape and metersticks to the lab stations.

Procedure Tips

1. The toys that students use should move reliably in a straight line and not too fast.
2. If it is practical, have students orient their arrangement so that marker 1 is north of the start position and marker 2 is east (or west) of the start position. Students can then use the terms *north*, *east*, or *west* in their velocity descriptions.

Sample Data

Trial	Time to Marker 1 (s)	Trial	Time to Marker 2 (s)
1	2.0 s	1	1.7 s
2	2.3 s	2	2.2 s
3	1.8 s	3	2.1 s
Average Time (s)	2.0 s	Average Time (s)	2.0 s
Average Speed (m/s)	1 m/2.0 s = 0.5 m/s	Average Speed (m/s)	1 m/2.0 s = 0.5 m/s

Answers

1. Students should find that speeds were about the same in Steps 3 and 4. Velocities were different in Steps 3 and 4. Velocities were different although the speeds were about the same because the car moved in different directions.
2. Sample Answer: I measured the average speed of the toy in both directions. Then I stated the velocities by stating both the speed and direction for the two different directions.

Quick Lab

Motion Graphs

Unlocking the Key Concept

This activity will help students understand that motion can be represented on a graph of distance versus time. The graph can then be analyzed to determine velocity and changes in velocity.

Inquiry Focus

Graph—organizing data in a visual way to show the relationship of one variable to another. In this case, students examine the relationship of time to distance traveled for a moving object

Group Size Groups

Class Time 15 minutes

Advance Preparation (10 minutes)

1. A steel tape of the type that builders and landscapers use would be best.
2. Find a suitable location for the activity. Someplace outside where students can walk steadily in a straight line for one minute without stopping is best.

Procedure Tips

1. You may need to modify the time intervals depending on the length of your measuring tape and the speed at which students walk.
2. Encourage students to walk at a steady pace so they obtain a straight-line graph.
3. Draw students' attention to the motion graphs in the text. Remind students that to graph motion, time and distance traveled are measured.
4. If the tape is not metric, have students multiply feet by 0.305 to obtain meters.

Answers

1. The graph would rise but in an irregular zigzag way.
2. Sample Answer: My graph rose steadily until 40 seconds when it went down slightly.
3. If the graph is a straight line, then the person walked at a steady speed.

Acceleration

Answering the Big Question

The activities in this lesson will help students answer the Big Question by having them measure and compare the different times needed to walk a specific distance while accelerating at different rates, understand acceleration in terms of change in velocity, and graph distance versus time.

Inquiry Warm-Up

Will You Hurry Up?

Inquiry Focus

Measure—collecting quantitative data about the acceleration and speed of a walker

Group Size Groups

Class Time 15 minutes

Advance Preparation

A steel tape of the type that builders and landscapers use would be best.

Procedure Tips

1. Shorter distances may be used, but the full 10-m distance allows students to try to achieve constant acceleration.
2. If you have students in hand-powered wheelchairs, ask them to accelerate through the course and then describe to the class how they achieved acceleration.
3. If the tape is not metric, have students multiply feet by 0.305 to obtain meters.

Answers

1. Students should observe the greatest acceleration in Step 3.
2. The walker should reach the greatest velocity in Step 3.
3. Look for answers that indicate that students continued to accelerate because slowing to a stop is also acceleration—negative acceleration.
4. Sample Answer: As positive acceleration occurs, velocity increases, and the time to cover the distance decreases.

Quick Lab

Describing Acceleration

Unlocking the Key Concept

This activity will help students understand the concept of acceleration as a change in velocity of an object and as one of the factors in describing the motion of objects.

Inquiry Focus

Measure—collecting quantitative data to determine the time required for a marble to roll various distances down a ramp

Group Size Groups

Class Time 15 minutes

Advance Preparation (10 minutes)

Distribute boards, books and other materials to the lab stations. The boards should be smooth enough that the marble rolls freely. The two meter sticks provide a channel for the marble to travel down.

Alternative Materials

Anything that is long enough can be made into a smooth, slanted ramp. You might choose to tape the meter sticks directly on to the table and prop up one end of the table with blocks.

Procedure Tips

1. The board should rest firmly on the books at one end, and on the table at the other. If the board is tilted, the marble may roll off the edge.
2. Have one team member do a "3-2-1-go" countdown to help students release the marble and start the stopwatch at the same instant.
3. If the marble rolls too fast for students to time, remove a book to lower the slope.
4. If the time for one of the trials is much different from the other two, students should eliminate it and do a fourth trial.

Answers

1. The marble covered the second half-meter (from 0.5 to 1.0 m) faster than it covered the first half-meter (from 0 to 0.5 m). The marble must have gained speed as it rolled down the ramp.
2. The marble rolled in the same direction each time, so it did not change direction. However its speed increased, so its velocity increased. Thus it accelerated.

Quick Lab

Graphing Acceleration

Unlocking the Key Concept

This activity will help students understand why a distance-versus-time graph is a curved line for an accelerating object.

Inquiry Focus

Graph—using real data to plot distance versus time

Group Size Large groups (8 students)

Class Time 15 minutes

Procedure Tips

The gym or cafeteria could be used instead of a hallway.

Sample Data

Students' graphs should curve up and to the right. The curve should flatten out with time.

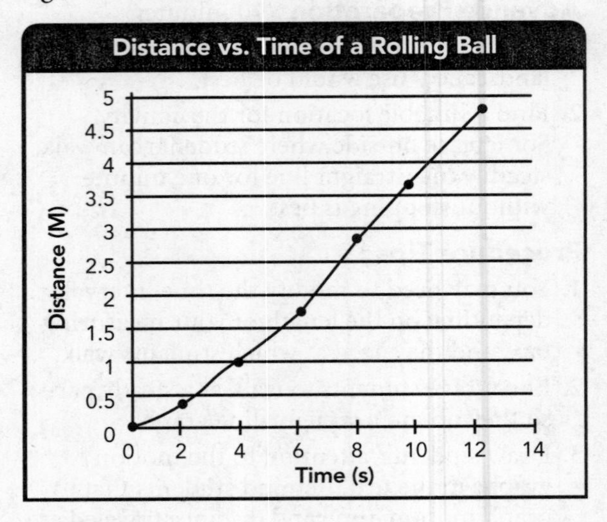

Answers

1. It represents the speed of the ball. The curve gets less steep with time.
2. Sample Answer: The change in slope—the curve getting less steep with time—means that the speed of the ball is decreasing.

Name ______________________ Date ______________ Class ______________

Inquiry Warm-Up

What Is Motion?

An object is in motion if its position changes relative to another object. To determine whether an object moves, you compare its position with a reference point.

INQUIRY FOCUS Draw Conclusions

Procedure

1. Place the paper on the floor so that it lies flat. Make a mark about 20 cm from one end of the paper. This mark will be the starting line. Use the meter stick to measure a distance of 1 m from the first mark. Make a second mark on the paper 1 m from the first mark. This is the finish line.
2. Put a piece of masking tape on the floor in line with the starting line on the paper.
3. Place the toy on the paper at the starting line. Start the toy and watch it as it moves toward the finish line.
4. Return the toy to the starting line. Grasp the paper at the end nearest the starting line. Start the toy so that it moves toward the finish line. Pull the paper backward in order to keep the toy in line with the tape on the floor, but allow the car to move toward the finish line on the paper.
5. When the toy reaches the finish line, stop the toy and stop pulling the paper.

Materials

- smooth paper, 2 m long
- wind-up or battery-powered toy
- meter stick
- masking tape
- marker

Think It Over

1. Review the definition of motion. Was the toy in motion in Step 3? Explain.

____

____

2. What reference point(s) did you use in Step 3?

____

____

3. Was the toy in motion in Step 4? Explain.

____

____

Name ______________________ Date ____________ Class ____________

Quick Lab

Identifying Motion

An object is in motion if its position changes relative to a reference point. An object's motion appears different to observers who are in different positions relative to the object and relative to the reference points.

INQUIRY FOCUS **Observe**

Procedure

1. Arrange your group so that they stand shoulder to shoulder in a line. Stand in front of your group with one side facing the your group and gently toss the tennis ball straight up. Catch it when it comes down. **CAUTION:** ***Throw the ball up and down; do not throw the ball at anyone or anything.***
2. Observe the ball's motion, and ask the group to observe the ball's motion.
3. Now walk slowly in front of the group from one end to the other while tossing the ball and catching it as before.
4. Again, observe the ball's motion, and ask the group to observe the ball's motion.

Materials

tennis ball

Think It Over

1. When the person with the ball was standing still, how did the observations of the ball's motion compare between the group and the person tossing the ball?

____

____

2. When the person with the ball was walking, how did the observations of the ball's motion compare between the group and the person tossing the ball? Explain why the observations differ.

____

____

____

____

Name ______________________ Date __________ Class __________

Inquiry Warm-Up

How Fast and How Far?

Motion refers to movement in a straight line, movement that changes direction, movement that stops and starts, and combinations of all of these.

INQUIRY FOCUS **Form an Operational Definition**

Procedure

Materials

- masking tape
- meter stick
- stopwatch

1. Place a strip of masking tape on the floor. Use a meter stick to measure a distance of 5 m from the first strip, and place a second strip of tape on the floor.
2. Using a stopwatch, time how long it takes you to walk 5 m at a normal pace. Record your time. __________
3. Now determine how far you can walk in 5 seconds if you walk at a normal pace. Record your distance. __________
4. Repeat Steps 2 and 3, walking slower than your normal pace. Then repeat Steps 2 and 3 walking faster than your normal pace.

____

____

Think It Over

1. Use the equation of Speed = Distance × Time to calculate your speed in Steps 2 and 3.

____

____

2. Now calculate your speed in the two parts of Step 4.

____

____

3. Describe the relationship among the distance you walk, the time it takes you to walk, and your walking speed.

____

____

PRE LAB

Stopping on a Dime

Reviewing Content

An object in motion has three properties. Distance refers to how far the object has moved from its starting point. Time refers to how long the object has been in motion. The speed of an object is equal to the distance the object moves per unit of time. To determine average speed, you divide the distance traveled by the length of time of the whole trip. For example, suppose you travel 800 km in 12 hours. Your average speed is 800 km ÷ 12 h = 67 km/h.

do the math!

Suppose a runner crosses the 25-m mark 8.6 s after starting. Calculate, in meters per second, the runner's average speed over the 25-m distance.

Average speed = _____

Reviewing Inquiry Focus

When you interpret data, you analyze the data and draw conclusions from it. Usually, making tables or graphs of the data helps you see the overall meaning of the data. In this lab, you will obtain data by timing events and measuring distances. You will examine tables of data to determine students' reaction times and how long it takes to stop after running a distance. From this data you will draw conclusions about the safe distance gymnasiums must have to allow players to stop after crossing the out-of-bounds line on a basketball court.

With these statements in mind, preview the Lab Investigation. Then answer the questions in the spaces provided.

1. What is the data you will collect in Part 1?

____

____

2. In Part 2, why is it important that the runner not slow down until they cross the 25-m mark?

____

____

3. What do you need to know in order to calculate the average speed of a runner?

____

____

Name________________ Date________ Class________

DIRECTED Inquiry — 40 min

Stopping on a Dime

Problem

INQUIRY FOCUS
Calculate, Interpret Data

What is the distance needed between an out-of-bounds line on a basketball court and a wall, so that a player can stop before hitting the wall?

Materials

wooden meter stick
tape measure
2 stopwatches or watches with second hands

Procedure

Part 1: Reaction Time

1. Have your partner suspend a wooden meter stick, zero end down, between your thumb and index finger, as shown. Your thumb and index finger should be about 3 cm apart.

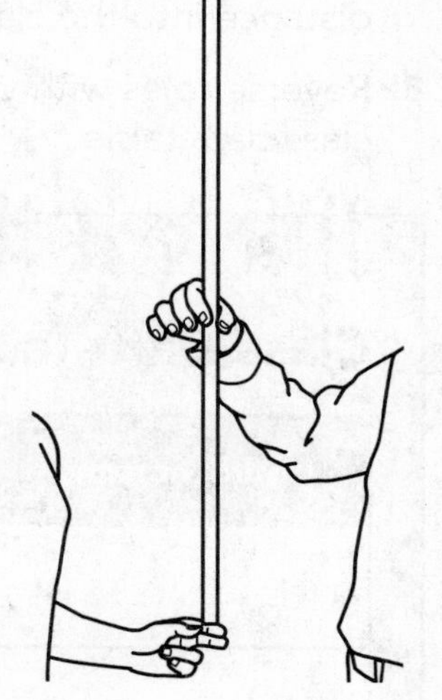

2. Your partner will drop the meter stick without giving you any warning. Try to grab it with your thumb and index finger.
3. Note the level at which you grabbed the meter stick and use the chart below to determine your reaction time. Record the time in the class data table.

Reaction Time

Distance (cm)	Time (s)	Distance (cm)	Time (s)
15	0.175	25	0.226
16	0.181	26	0.230
17	0.186	27	0.235
18	0.192	28	0.239
19	0.197	29	0.243
20	0.202	30	0.247
21	0.207	31	0.252
22	0.212	32	0.256
23	0.217	33	0.260
24	0.221	34	0.263

4. Reverse roles with your partner and repeat Steps 1–3.

Part 2: Stopping Distance

5. On the school field or in the gymnasium, mark off a distance of 25 m. **CAUTION: *Be sure to remove any obstacles from the course.***

6. Have your partner time how long it takes you to run the course at full speed. After you pass the 25-m mark, come to a stop as quickly as possible and remain standing. You must not slow down before the mark.

7. Have your partner measure the distance from the 25-m mark to your final position. This is the distance you need to come to a complete stop. Enter your time and distance into the class data table.

8. Reverse roles with your partner. Enter your partner's time and distance into the class data table.

Class Data Table

Student name	Reaction time (s)	Running time (s)	Stopping distance (m)

Analyze and Conclude

1. **Calculate** Calculate the average speed of the student who ran the 25-m course the fastest.

____

____

____

2. **Infer** Multiply the average speed of the fastest student by the slowest reaction time listed in the class data table. Why would you be interested in this number?

____

____

____

3. **Interpret Data** Add the distance calculated in Question 2 to the longest stopping distance in the class data table. What does this total distance represent?

____

____

4. **Draw Conclusions** Explain why it is important to use the fastest speed, the slowest reaction time, and the longest stopping distance in your calculations.

____

____

____

5. **Design an Experiment** What other factors should you take into account to get results that apply to a real basketball court?

____

____

____

Name ______________________ Date ____________ Class ____________

POST LAB

Stopping on a Dime

1. **Design an Experiment** How could you modify the experiment to determine the reaction time of a runner crossing a visible line rather than catching a dropped meter stick?

2. **Draw Conclusions** When you run out of bounds on a basketball court, what factors determine how long it takes you to stop? List as many as you think will apply.

3. **Summarize** Describe what you learned about providing a safety zone between the out-of-bounds line and the wall of a gym. Write any questions you still have.

What I learned

What I still want to know

Communicate

Design a Solution Suppose you calculate that the distance from the out-of-bounds line to the wall of the basketball court is too short for safety. Write a proposal to the school that describes the problem. In your proposal, suggest a strategy for making the court safer.

Name _______________ Date _______________ Class _______________

OPEN Inquiry

Stopping on a Dime

Problem

INQUIRY FOCUS
Calculate, Draw Conclusions

What is the distance needed between an out-of-bounds line on a basketball court and a wall, so that a player can stop before hitting the wall?

Materials

wooden meter stick
tape measure
2 stopwatches or watches with second hands

Design an Experiment

1. You are designing a new basketball court to be built between two buildings. Safety will be an important consideration. You will determine the minimum distance needed between an out-of-bounds line and a wall so that players can stop before hitting the wall.
2. To determine the minimum distance needed, you will perform two experiments. In the first experiment, you will determine reaction times of group members. In the second experiment, you will determine maximum running speeds, how long it takes them to stop, and the distance over which they stop.
3. In your first experiment, have one member of your group hold the meter stick with the zero end down, between their thumb and index finger. Hold your thumb and index finger about 3 cm apart, positioned even with the zero on the meter stick.
4. The group member holding the meter stick will drop it. Try to grab it as quickly as possible between your fingers.
5. Using the chart below, determine your reaction time.

Reaction Time

Distance (cm)	Time (s)	Distance (cm)	Time (s)
15	0.175	25	0.226
16	0.181	26	0.230
17	0.186	27	0.235
18	0.192	28	0.239
19	0.197	29	0.243
20	0.202	30	0.247
21	0.207	31	0.252
22	0.212	32	0.256
23	0.217	33	0.260
24	0.221	34	0.263

6. With your group, design a data table in which to record the reaction time of each group member. Have your teacher check your data table.
7. Test the reaction time of every member of your group.
8. Design an experiment to determine the maximum speed and the stopping time of everyone in your group. These studies may be conducted on the school field or in the gymnasium. In designing your experiment, keep in mind:

- basketball players may be moving at full speed when they determine that they have to stop.
- if you know someone's top speed and reaction time, you can figure out how far he or she will continue to run after noticing he or she has crossed the out-of-bounds line.

9. Write a detailed procedure and create a data table in which to record your results. Have your teacher check your procedure and table.
10. Conduct your experiment.

Procedure

____

____

____

____

____

____

Data Table

Analyze and Conclude

1. **Calculate** Calculate the average speed in m/s of the fastest member of your group.

2. **Infer** Multiply the speed of the fastest student (calculated in Question 1) by the slowest reaction time in your group. Why would you select these two numbers?

3. **Interpret Data** Add the distance calculated in Question 2 to the longest stopping distance in your group. What does this total distance represent?

4. **Draw Conclusions** Explain why it is important to use the fastest speed, the slowest reaction time, and the longest stopping distance in your calculations.

Name ____________ Date ____________ Class ____________

OPEN Inquiry — Lab Investigation

POST LAB

Stopping on a Dime

1. **Control Variables** What potential variables existed in your experiment? How did you control them?

2. **Design an Experiment** What other factors should you take into account to get results that apply to a real basketball court?

3. **Infer** In what other settings might reaction times and stopping times be used to determine whether a setting is safe for a given activity?

4. **Summarize** Describe what you learned about providing a safety zone between the out-of-bounds line and the wall of a gym. Write any questions you still have.

What I learned

What I still want to know

Communicate

Design a Solution Suppose you calculate that the distance from the out-of-bounds line to the wall of the basketball court is too short for safety. Write a proposal to the school that describes the problem and how you came to the conclusion that the court is unsafe. In your proposal, suggest a strategy for making the court safer.

Name ______________________ Date ______________ Class ______________

Quick Lab

Velocity

In this activity, you will investigate the difference between speed and velocity.

INQUIRY FOCUS Form an Operational Definition

Procedure

1. Stick a small piece of masking tape on the floor. Use the meter stick to measure 1 m from that spot. Place a 12-cm strip of tape perpendicular to the meter stick at the 1-m distance.
2. From the first spot, measure a 1-m distance out to the side, 90° from the first measurement. Place another 12-cm strip of tape perpendicular to the meter stick.
3. Place the toy at the first spot, release it, and let it move to the first 1-m marker. Measure how long it takes for the toy to travel to the first marker. Repeat twice more. Record your times in the data table below.
4. Repeat Step 3, but aim the toy toward the second 1-m marker.
5. Calculate the average speed and time of travel for both trials. Record your answers in the data table.

Materials

masking tape
meter stick
wind-up or battery-powered toy
stopwatch

Data Table

Trial	Time to Marker 1 (s)	Trial	Time to Marker 2 (s)
1	1	1	
2	2	2	
3	3	3	
Average Time (s)		Average Time (s)	
Average Speed (m/s)		Average Speed (m/s)	

Think It Over

1. Were the speeds the same in Steps 3 and 4? Were the velocities the same in Steps 3 and 4? Why or why not?

____

____

2. Describe how you determined and stated the average velocity of the toy.

____

____

Name ______________________ Date ____________ Class ____________

Quick Lab

15 min

Motion Graphs

One way to study the motion of an object is to graph the distance moved versus time. The shape of the graph will show whether or not the object moved at a constant speed.

INQUIRY FOCUS Graph

Materials

masking tape
measuring tape
stopwatch
pencils
graph paper
ruler

Procedure

1. Mark a starting line as your teacher directs.
2. ⚠ Have one group member start at the line and walk at a normal pace. *Note: Take care when walking.*
3. Have another group member mark with tape the distance traveled at 10-second intervals for 1 min.
4. Use a measuring tape to measure the distance traveled during each time period. Record this data.

____

____

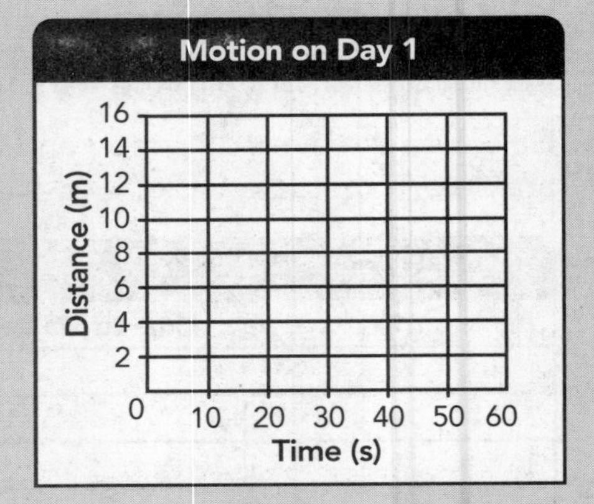

5. Plot your data on the graph on the right. Connect the points to make a line graph. For help, refer to the graph entitled "Motion on Day 1" in your student edition.

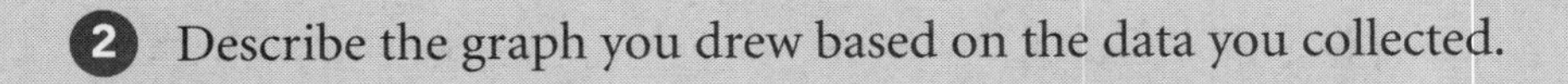

Think It Over

1. If a person speeds up and slows down, what shape of graph would you expect?

____

____

2. Describe the graph you drew based on the data you collected.

____

____

3. Based on your graph, how would you describe the motion of the person who walked?

____

____

Name ______________________ Date ____________ Class ____________

Inquiry Warm-Up

15 min

Will You Hurry Up?

Whenever an object's velocity changes, the object accelerates. If the object speeds up, it is accelerating. The object also accelerates when it slows down. When an object slows down, the acceleration is negative.

INQUIRY FOCUS Measure

Procedure

1. Measure a distance of 10 m in an open area. Mark the distance with masking tape.
2. ⚠ Walk the 10 m in such a way that you keep moving faster throughout the entire distance. Have a partner time you. **CAUTION:** ***Be careful when you are walking.***
3. Repeat Step 2, walking the 10 m in less time than you did before. Remember to keep speeding up throughout the entire 10 m.
4. Repeat Step 3, but this time walk the distance in twice the time as in Step 2.

Materials

measuring tape
masking tape
stopwatch

Think It Over

1. In which step did you accelerate the most? Explain.

____

____

2. In which step did you move at the greatest velocity?

____

____

3. After you crossed the 10-m mark, did you continue to accelerate? Explain.

____

____

4. How is the change in your speed related to the time in which you walked the 10-m course?

____

____

Name ______________________ Date ______________ Class ______________

Quick Lab

Describing Acceleration

When an object's speed or direction changes, the object accelerates. If it speeds up, the acceleration is positive. If it slows down, acceleration is negative.

INQUIRY FOCUS **Measure**

Procedure

1. Tape the meter sticks lengthwise (1 cm apart) to the board to make a channel in which the marble will roll.
2. Place pieces of tape at 0 m, 0.5 m, and 1.0 m on a meter stick.
3. Place one end of the board on top of a stack of 3 books to form a ramp.
4. Place a marble at the 0-m mark. Have your partner time how long it takes the marble to roll to the 0.5-m mark. Record the time. Repeat this step 2 more times.
5. Repeat Step 4, but this time measure from 0 m to 1.0 m.
6. Calculate the average time for the marble to roll from 0 m to 0.5 m and from 0 m to 1.0 m. Subtract these times to obtain an average time for 0.5 to 1.0 m.

Materials

- marble
- board, 1 m long
- 2 meter sticks
- masking tape
- marker
- books
- stopwatch

Data Table

Trial	0 to 0.5 m time (s)	0 to 1.0 m time
1		
2		
3		
Average Time (s)		
0.5 m to 1.0 m Average Time		

Think It Over

1. Compare the average 0- to 0.5-m time with the average 0.5- to 1.0-m time. How can you account for any difference you observed?

____

____

2. Acceleration is a change in velocity. Did the velocity of the marble change? Explain.

____

____

Name ______________________ Date ____________ Class ____________

Quick Lab

Graphing Acceleration

Whenever an object speeds up or slows down, the object accelerates. In this activity, you will collect data to make a distance-versus-time graph.

INQUIRY FOCUS Graph

Procedure

1. Toward the end of a long hallway, place seven strips of masking tape 2 m apart.
2. One group member should kneel at each of the strips. An eighth group member should roll the ball down the hallway. The ball should be rolled at such an initial speed that it stops soon after it passes the last strip of tape. You can practice this. Everyone except the one at the first strip should have stopwatches.
3. The person at the first strip of tape should call out "Now!" just as the ball touches the tape. At that point, all group members should start their stopwatches.
4. Group members should stop their watches when the ball reaches their strip.
5. Record the distance and time of the ball at each strip of tape.
6. Repeat Steps 3–5 two more times. Calculate the average time at each point.
7. Use the data and graph paper to make a distance-versus-time graph. Plot the average time on the horizontal axis. Plot distance on the vertical axis.

Materials

- tennis ball
- meter stick or measuring tape
- masking tape
- 6 stopwatches
- graph paper

	Distance (m)	Strip 1	Strip 2	Strip 3	Strip 4	Strip 5	Strip 6	Strip 7
Time (s)	Trial 1							
	Trial 2							
	Trial 3							
	Average Time							

Think It Over

1. What does the graph's slope represent? How does the slope change with time?

____

____

2. How does the change in slope show what happens to the speed of the ball?

____

____

CHAPTER 2

TABLE OF CONTENTS

Forces

Teacher Notes 27

The Nature of Force

Inquiry Warm-Up — Is the Force With You? 37

Quick Lab — What Is Force? 38

Quick Lab — Modeling Unbalanced Forces 39

Friction and Gravity

Inquiry Warm-Up — Observing Friction 40

Lab Investigation — Sticky Sneakers
- *Pre Lab* 41
- *Directed Inquiry* 42
- *Open Inquiry* 46

Quick Lab — Calculating 50

Newton's Laws of Motion

Inquiry Warm-Up — What Changes Motion? 51

Quick Lab — Around and Around 52

Quick Lab — Newton's Second Law 53

Quick Lab — Interpreting Illustrations 54

Momentum

Inquiry Warm-Up — How Pushy Is a Straw? 55

Quick Lab — Colliding Cars 56

Free Fall and Circular Motion

Inquiry Warm-Up — What Makes an Object Move in a Circle? 57

Quick Lab — Which Lands First? 58

Quick Lab — Orbiting Earth 59

The Nature of Force

Answering the Big Question

The activities in this lesson will help students answer the Big Question by showing them how forces are described and allowing them to see how the motion of an object is affected when different combinations of forces are applied to that object.

Inquiry Warm-Up

Is the Force With You?

Inquiry Focus

Observe—gathering information about how varying amounts of force applied to an object affect the motion of the object

Group Size Groups

Class Time 15 minutes

Alternative Materials

Any small cart with wheels, such as a ballistics cart, can substitute for the skateboard.

Safety

Students should wear safety goggles throughout the activity.

Procedure Tips

1. Each pair of spring scales should have the same capacity and units.
2. If the spring scale is calibrated in grams, multiply by 0.01 to obtain the approximate value in newtons.
3. The spring scale should not be angled to the side or up and down while it is used, or the measurements will not be accurate.
4. Both students should stop pulling on their spring scale before either student lets go of their spring scale.

Answers

1. The skateboard did not move when both pulled with the same force.
2. Sample Answer: The skateboard moved slightly until the reading on one spring scale was equal to the force on the other spring scale.
3. Sample Answer: While the forces were unequal, the skateboard moved slowly in the direction of the greater force.

Quick Lab

What Is Force?

Unlocking the Key Concept

This activity will help students understand the concept of a force as a push or a pull in a specific direction.

Inquiry Focus

Infer—suggesting a possible explanation or drawing a conclusion about two opposing forces applied to the same object and how they affect its motion

Group Size Pairs

Class Time 10 minutes

Materials

Try to use large washers about 2 inches in diameter so that students can easily hook spring scales to them. Also, a large washer makes a distinct third object on which to apply forces. Ideally, students won't think of it just as a connector for the two scales.

Safety

1. Students should wear their safety goggles throughout the activity.
2. Caution students not to pull too hard or play tug-of-war. Spring scales can break and produce dangerous flying pieces.

Procedure Tips

1. If it is hard to hook the scales to the washer, instruct students to tie two loops of string to the washers and hook the scales to those.
2. If the scales can be zeroed, have students do so before they begin.

Answers

1. Students should realize that they exerted force in exactly opposite directions.
2. The washer should not have moved. Students should infer that they were exerting opposite, balanced forces on the washer.
3. Sample Answer: The washer moved in the direction of the greater force because the forces that were acting on it were no longer equal.

Quick Lab

Modeling Unbalanced Forces

Unlocking the Key Concept

This activity will help students understand that an object moves only when unequal forces are acting on it.

Make Models—creating a physical representation of unequal forces acting on an object and observing the results

Group Size 2 large groups

Class Time 10 minutes

Safety

Remind students that this is a scientific demonstration, not a competition. They should not pull so hard as to cause students to lose their balance.

Procedure Tips

1. If your classroom is small you may want to use a shorter length of rope.
2. Caution the teams to pull only until one side moves.
3. Assign four students to one team and six students to the other team. The teams should pull until one side moves.

Answers

1. Sample Answer: One team was able to pull with more force.
2. The net force is in the direction of the winning team.
3. Look for answers that indicate that one force is stronger than the other, the forces are not equal, or the forces are unbalanced.

Friction and Gravity

Answering the Big Question

The activities in this lesson will help students answer the Big Question by having them observe how friction is affected by the surfaces involved and by identifying the relationship between weight, mass, and Earth's gravity.

Inquiry Warm-Up

Observing Friction

Inquiry Focus

Observe—using the senses to gather information about the relationship between the friction and a variety of different surfaces

Group Size Pairs or groups

Class Time 15 minutes

Materials

1. The small, heavy object should have a flat bottom 75 to 100 mm in diameter and a mass of 200 to 500 g.
2. Use very fine sandpaper; 600 grit is ideal.

Advance Preparation

1. Obtain sandpaper. Cut the sandpaper and notebook sheets in half along the short dimension.
2. Cut the wax paper sheets to about the same size as the cut notebook paper sheets.

Alternative Materials

A small can of fruit or vegetables placed on an old CD or DVD can be used for the small, heavy object.

Procedure Tips

1. The small, heavy object should have a flat bottom 75 to 100 mm in diameter and a mass of 200 to 500 g.
2. Students should not pull the sheets of paper too rapidly or they may tear.
3. Instruct students to be sure to place the rough sides of the sandpaper against each other.
4. Caution students not to rub the rough side of the sandpaper on the surface of the lab table.

Answers

1. The wax paper felt very smooth. The notebook paper felt less smooth than the wax paper. The sandpaper felt rough.
2. Sandpaper required the greatest force to pull it; wax paper required the least.
3. Sample Answer: When sliding, smooth surfaces produce less friction than rough surfaces.

Lab Investigation

Sticky Sneakers

Unlocking the Key Concept

Both Versions This activity will help students understand some of the factors that affect the force of friction between two surfaces—the sole of a sneaker and a tabletop (or floor). In order to confine the observations to the effectiveness of the sneaker sole, students will use shoes of equal mass, therefore of equal weight. Thus, each shoe will press on the table with equal force.

Answers—Pre Lab

Both Versions:

1. Students will measure the mass of the shoes in grams or kilograms, and the force needed to pull them in newtons.
2. Sample Answer: If the shoes have equal mass, they will have equal weight because Earth's gravity will attract them with the same force.

Inquiry Focus

Directed Inquiry:

Interpret Data—analyzing and drawing conclusions from data including differences between control and experimental groups; comparing friction-force data from pulling three different sneakers adjusted to have equal weight, and concluding which brand of sneaker has the most friction with the tabletop

Open Inquiry:

Control Variables—designing an experiment to test the role of friction between the ground and the sole of a sneaker

Predict—making hypotheses based on observations of sneakers and surfaces

Interpret Data—recording data and drawing conclusions about how friction is related to sneakers and surfaces

Group Size

Both Versions Pairs or groups

Class Time

Directed Inquiry 45 minutes

Open Inquiry 60 minutes

Materials

Surfaces can include carpet squares, tile, sandpaper, or linoleum. If possible, students can use various outdoor surfaces such as grass, cement, dirt, asphalt, or turf.

Safety

Both Versions:

1. Spring scales should be used carefully so the springs do not break.
2. Review the Laboratory Safety Rules at the front of this book.

Advance Preparation (30 minutes)

Both Versions:

1. Assemble the spring scales, paper clips, tape, balance, and mass sets.
2. Bring in an assortment of sneakers and/or ask students to bring extra sneakers from home.

Procedure Tips

Directed Inquiry:

1. Demonstrate how to zero and use a spring scale. If the spring scale is calibrated in grams, have students multiply grams by 0.01 to obtain the approximate value in newtons.
2. Show students how to measure the force of sliding friction with a spring scale by pulling an object with a slow, constant motion. Emphasize that they should watch the scale, not the shoe and try to pull so that the force remains constant. This may take some practice.
3. Tell students to pull an object forward to measure forward-stopping friction and sideways to measure sideways-stopping friction.
4. Students may get better results if they wipe dirt and dust off the sole of the shoe with a wet paper towel. This will expose clean rubber.
5. The spring scale should not be angled to the side or up and down while it is being used, or the measurements will not be accurate.

Open Inquiry:

1. Begin by asking students to examine the bottom of their shoes and discuss the differences in shoe soles. Ask, **Why do some shoes have a lot of tread while others don't?** *(Shoes have many different uses, so there are different styles.)* Ask, **How is the sole of the shoe related to the shoe's intended use?** *(Shoes used for athletics, hiking, etc., require*

more tread to grip surfaces. Other shoes may require lighter grip with a surface, so they might have smooth soles.) Lead the discussion toward friction. Ask, **How does the tread on sneakers affect stopping, starting, and sideways friction?** *(The more tread a sneaker has, the more friction it will have, which will make it easier to stop, start, and move sideways.)* Have several students demonstrate these three types of friction. Ask, **What does friction depend on?** *(adhesion of the two surfaces that are coming together, force of gravity or other forces pushing those surfaces together)*

2. Name and display the materials that students will use in this activity. Limit the number of variables in their experiment by encouraging students to choose either a variety of sneakers or a variety of surfaces.
3. Demonstrate how to zero and use the spring scales. Show the students how to attach the paper clips to the shoe and then the spring scale to the paper clips. Show them how to measure the force of sliding friction with a spring scale by pulling an object with a slow, constant motion.
4. Tell students to pull an object backward to measure starting friction, forward to measure forward-stopping friction, and sideways for sideways-stopping friction.

Sample Data

See the sample data table below.

Answers—Analyze and Conclude

Directed Inquiry:

1. Students' answers will depend on the types of shoes tested. In general, running shoes have more starting friction, basketball shoes exert more forward stopping friction, and tennis shoes exert more sideways-stopping friction. The amount of wear will have a large effect, also.
2. The manipulated variable is which sneaker is used. The responding variable is the amount of friction. The weight of the shoes is constant.
3. Look for answers that show an understanding of the relationship between friction and motion. Friction is a force that acts in the opposite direction of motion. So, just as the sneaker begins moving, the spring scale shows the amount of friction opposing motion.
4. Sample Answer: No; in actual use there is much more mass in the sneakers, therefore more weight pressing the sneakers to the surface. Also, the way a person stands causes the sneaker sole to flex, changing the way the sole contacts the floor.
5. Sample Answer: You pull the sneaker at a slow speed to test stopping friction because your sneaker is sliding slowly along the ground or floor when you stop running. You pull a sneaker that is not moving to test starting friction because your sneaker is not moving when you start running.
6. Students' answers may state that one brand of sneaker provides better traction than another because the soles are made of different materials, have different tread designs, or have different amounts of wear.

Open Inquiry:

1. Look for answers that indicate that frictional force is affected by the types of surfaces involved and how large a force pushes the surfaces together. Mass affects this because an object with greater mass will probably press the surfaces together more.
2. Look for data that show sneakers with more tread have a greater frictional force or that rougher surfaces have greater frictional force against the shoe. Experimental support of predictions will depend on each student's prediction.

Sample Data Table—Open Inquiry

Type of Shoe	Type of Surface					
	Lawn	Concrete	Asphalt	Tile	Rug	Wood
Sneaker	7.5 N	6.5 N	6 N	7.5 N	7 N	6 N
Soft Rubber—Lots of Tread	12 N	8 N	10 N	6.5 N	7 N	8 N
Hard Rubber—Smoother Surface	11 N	8 N	9 N	8 N	8 N	9.5 N

3. Sample Answer: The black shoe had the greatest starting frictional force. It also had the greatest stopping and sideways frictional force because it had a rough tread that covered all parts of the bottom of the shoe. The carpet had the greatest starting frictional force. It did not have the greatest stopping or sideways frictional force because when the shoe moved sideways, it went the same direction as the carpet fibers, making for a smooth interaction.
4. Sample Answer: My next step would be to test the sneakers using real people starting and stopping on different surfaces to see how they performed in real-world situations.

Answers—Post Lab

Directed Inquiry:

1. Students might suggest adding enough weight to the sneaker to more closely simulate the way the soles would contact the floor when they are being worn by a real person. They might also suggest actually having a person wear the shoes when they are being tested. Much larger scales would be needed. Another suggestion might be to compare only new shoes or shoes with equal amounts of wear.
2. Students cannot suggest skidding to a stop or running from a stop on a hard floor while wearing the shoes because that would damage the shoes. As in the lab, placing weight in the shoes and testing their friction on a smooth floor by pulling and pushing may help determine friction factors.
3. Generally, students will have observed different amounts of friction from the three different sneakers. Students might wonder how tread patterns or sole compositions affect friction.

Communicate—Students should relate their brochures to their own activities such as basketball, tennis, running, power walking, and other activities. Sports requiring cleats or spiked shoes, such as baseball, golf, or football cannot be considered. Students' diagrams should be clearly labeled with force arrows reflecting sizes and directions of the forces. They should tell why friction in these directions is desirable.

Open Inquiry:

1. Look for answers that discuss the relationship between the spikes or cleats and the amount of friction between the shoe and the ground. They increase the friction by digging directly into the surface.
2. Sample Answer: To make a safer tire, many of the same characteristics in a sneaker have to be present in a tire. The tire needs to have a lot of tread for gripping the road from all angles for starting, stopping, and even possible sideways stopping. It also has to be smooth enough to roll comfortably along the road at different speeds. Its tread should be thick enough to last over long periods of time and carry a lot of weight. The amount of tread on the tire will depend on uses of the car and road conditions. Heavier cars will require more tread than lightweight cars will require. Cars traveling in snow and ice require a different tread than tires traveling on hot and dry surfaces.
3. Generally, students will have observed different amounts of friction from either the three different sneakers or three different surfaces. Students might wonder how tread patterns or sole compositions affect friction.

Communicate—Student posters should show that they understand how friction is affected by the design of the sneaker sole. The poster should also clearly show how mass affects the frictional performance of any sneaker.

Quick Lab

Calculating

Unlocking the Key Concept

This activity will help students understand that the weight of an object is equal to the pull of Earth's gravity on an object and that an object's weight depends on its mass.

Inquiry Focus

Measure —collecting quantitative data using units of mass and weight to better understand the relationship between mass and weight, and to improve the ability to estimate the weight of objects

Group Size Pairs or groups

Class Time 20 minutes

Advance Preparation (5 minutes)
Distribute materials to lab stations. Try to have objects of varying masses at each station. Suggested objects include: books, shoes, spiral notebooks, scissors, small tools, any other objects likely to weigh between 0.5 N to 4 N (from about 2 oz to 1 lb).

Procedure Tips
1. If your time is limited, have students stop after Step 3.
2. Students may wonder about the factor 9.8 m/s^2.You may want to skip momentarily to Lesson 5 to have students read about the acceleration of gravity on Earth. The gravitational force exerted on an object is measured in newtons, which is 1 kg•m/s^2. So, the force is equal to the mass of an object in kg multiplied by 9.8 m/s^2.
3. Students can check the reasonableness of their answers by mentally multiplying the mass by 10.

Answers
1. Answers will vary, but students are likely to make errors because they are unfamiliar with the newton unit.
2. Students may make the largest errors on dense, metal objects or large, light objects because they tend to associate weight with size.
3. Student estimates are likely to improve somewhat as their familiarity with the units and actual weights of objects increases.

Newton's Laws of Motion

Answering the Big Question
The activities in this lesson will help students answer the Big Question by having students illustrate situations that demonstrate Newton's three laws of motion.

Inquiry Warm-Up
What Changes Motion?

Inquiry Focus
Predict—making an educated guess based on prior experience about the motion of a car and the loose objects it carries when the car is stopped by a barrier

Group Size Individuals or pairs

Class Time 10 minutes

Safety
Caution students not to roll cars violently, especially if they are heavy cars.

Advance Preparation (5 minutes)
Distribute materials to lab stations.

Alternative Materials
Anything that rolls freely and is not too heavy can serve as the car. Any dense objects that will stack can replace the washers.

Procedure Tips
1. Students should be reminded not to fasten the washers to the top of the car.
2. Students should hold the washers as they push the car forward. Otherwise, the washers will fall off the back of the car.
3. Books should be thick enough so that cars do not run over them.

Answers
1. The car stops after bouncing backward slightly.
2. The washers fly forward off the top of the car.
3. Sample Answer: A net force acts on the moving car, causing it to stop. The washers are free to move, so they continue moving forward.

Quick Lab
Around and Around

Unlocking the Key Concept
This activity will help students understand Newton's first law of motion by demonstrating a case in which motion changes as a result of changing a force.

Inquiry Focus
Infer—suggesting a possible explanation for the change in the direction of motion as centripetal force drops to zero

Group Size Pairs

Class Time 15 minutes

Safety

Caution students not to swing the balls around over their heads. The balls should remain close to the floor while they are being swung around.

Advance Preparation (5 minutes)

Distribute materials to lab stations. Tape can be either plastic tape or masking tape.

Alternative Materials

Any small, light, rubber or plastic balls can be used. Do not substitute heavy balls because their impact can cause injury or damage.

Procedure Tips

1. Students should tape 3 or 4 cm of string to the table tennis ball and press down firmly on the tape so that the string does not slip.
2. If students have trouble twirling the ball, add some mass (inertia) to the ball by wrapping two or three turns of masking tape around the ball.

Answers

1. Sample Answer: When the ball is released as it is moving in the forward direction, it will move directly away. This is at the 9 o'clock position if the ball is twirling clockwise.
2. Sample Answer: When the ball is released as it is moving in the backward direction, it will move directly toward the student. This is at the 3 o'clock position if the ball is twirling clockwise.
3. Look for answers that show students understand that the ball will continue in a straight line in the direction it is moving when the string is released.

Quick Lab

Newton's Second Law

Unlocking the Key Concept

This activity will help students understand that as the force on a constant mass is increased, the acceleration of that mass also increases—this is an illustration of Newton's second law.

Inquiry Focus

Infer—suggesting a possible explanation or drawing a conclusion about how the amount of force applied to an object affects its acceleration

Group Size Groups

Class Time 20 minutes

Materials

1. Large toy cars about 12 cm long are ideal for this exercise, although smaller cars may be used.
2. Cut lengths of string according to the size of your tables. Ideally, the washers will hit the floor just before the car reaches the end of the table.

Alternative Materials

Standardized masses can be used if you wish to have quantitative results.

Advance Preparation

Cut lengths of string according to the size of your tables. You may want to try this lab ahead of time in order to see how the setup works with your materials.

Procedure Tips

1. The use of three washers is only a guideline. The number of washers needed will vary depending on the mass of the car, the size of the washers, and how smooth the surface is.
2. In order to help students recognize the distinction between acceleration and velocity, have them repeat Step 5 until they can describe the car's acceleration as changing velocity.

Answers

1. The force of friction in the axles of the car is being overcome.
2. Sample Answer: The car accelerated to a faster velocity in Step 5.
3. Look for answers that describe the relationship between force, mass, and acceleration. More force was applied to the car in Step 5 because more weight was added to the hook. More weight (mass) resulted in a greater force applied to the car which resulted in a greater acceleration.

Quick Lab

Interpreting Illustrations

Unlocking the Key Concept

This activity will help students recognize and understand the pairs of action-reaction forces that illustrate Newton's third law.

Inquiry Focus

Make Models—creating mental or physical representations of an event and recognizing diagrams that model Newton's third law

Group Size Pairs or groups

Class Time 20 minutes

Advance Preparation

Ask students to contribute magazines two or three days before the activity. Magazines dealing with sports, sailing, skiing, golf, cars, and other action subjects may provide good examples. Examples may also be found in general news magazines.

Procedure Tips

Find one or two examples in the magazines and point out to students the action and reaction forces illustrated.

Answers

1. Look for answers that show students can correctly identify the action-reaction pair. For example, a baseball bat striking a ball exerts as much force on the ball as the ball exerts on the bat during any part of the swing.
2. Sample Answer: As the person steps on the ice, the slippery surface of the ice cannot exert as much force on the shoe as the dry concrete did. The action-reaction forces between the ice and the shoe are less and the shoe slips on the ice as the person attempts to move forward.

Momentum

Answering the Big Question

The activities in this lesson will help students answer the Big Question by having them observe the resulting motion of two objects having different masses when the same force is applied to each object and by having them model collisions in order to observe how momentum is conserved.

Inquiry Warm-Up

How Pushy Is a Straw?

Inquiry Focus

Develop a Hypothesis—using prior knowledge or experience to state the expected relationship between the force applied to an object, the mass of the object, and the speed at which the object moves

Group Size Pairs

Class Time 10 minutes

Alternative Materials

Steel ball bearings can replace the marbles.

Procedure Tips

1. Use straws with a large diameter as small diameter straws are likely to bend.
2. Make sure students do not use a twisting motion when they release the straw.
3. Be sure that students release the book and the straw at the same time.

Answers

1. Sample Answer: The book and the straw move in opposite directions, and the straw moves faster than the book.
2. Look for answers that indicate the objects will have closer speeds if they are closer in mass.

Quick Lab

Colliding Cars

Unlocking the Key Concept

This activity will help students understand that momentum is conserved in any type of collision between objects by having them observe the results of several types of collisions.

Inquiry Focus

Predict—making an educated guess based on previous knowledge and observations about how the momentum of objects involved in a collision changes so that total momentum is conserved

Group Size Pairs

Class Time 10 minutes

Procedure Tips

1. The toy cars should have approximately the same mass and low-friction wheels.
2. Toy cars or trucks with relatively flat, vertical front and back surfaces work best.
3. Show students how to make a tape loop by rolling the tape loosely around their finger.
4. Sample Prediction for Procedure Step 4: The cars will continue in the direction that the faster car is moving.

Answers

1. Sample Answer: The cars stuck together, the stationary car started moving in the same direction as the moving car, and the moving car slowed down but continued in the same direction.
2. Sample Answer: My prediction was proved wrong because the cars came to a stop.
3. Momentum was conserved. The cars have equal and opposite momenta before colliding, and were at rest afterwards, resulting in a total momentum of zero before and after the collision.

Free Fall and Circular Motion

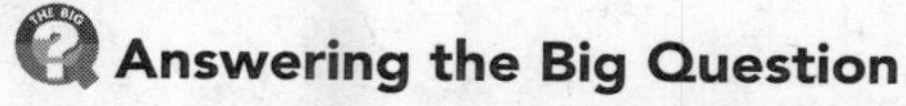

Answering the Big Question

The activities in this lesson will help students answer the Big Question by having them see how the force of gravity affects free fall and what forces are involved when one object orbits another object.

Inquiry Warm-Up

What Makes an Object Move in a Circle?

Inquiry Focus

Infer—suggesting an explanation for the cause of acceleration in an object moving in a circular path, based on observations of the motion of a tethered object as it moves at varying speeds

Group Size Individuals or pairs

Class Time 10 minutes

Safety

1. Students should make sure that no one is near enough to get hit with the swinging spool. Demonstrate a "circle of safety" to ensure no one gets hit.
2. Students should wear safety goggles during the activity.

Alternative Materials

Any small, dense object to which a string can be securely tied will work.

Procedure Tips

1. Medium-size thread spools provide the best results.
2. Suggest that students pass the string through the center of the spool before tying.
3. Tell students to pull on the string to make sure their string is securely tied.
4. Caution students not to swing the spool near another person.

Answers

1. The pulling force exerted by the string is greater when the spool is moving faster.
2. Students might predict that the spool would move more slowly or that it won't make it over the top. Both predictions are correct depending on how slowly the spool moves.
3. Look for answers that explain the relationship between the string and the spool in terms of force. The force pulling on the spool causes it to accelerate. I know the force and acceleration are related because I felt a stronger tug when I swung the spool faster and it had a greater acceleration.

Quick Lab

Which Lands First?

Unlocking the Key Concept

This activity will help students understand that the mass of an object does not affect the speed of that object during free fall.

Inquiry Focus

Design an Experiment—making an educated guess based on an observation about how to test the time required for objects of different mass to fall equal distances during free fall

Group Size Individuals or pairs

Class Time 15 minutes

Alternative Materials

Use large metal washers instead of the quarters.

Procedure Tips

1. Show students how to tape the coins together in a neat fashion.
2. Remind students to keep the ruler parallel to the edge of the desk.

Answers

1. There was no difference in the time the coins took to fall. Both the single coin and the three coin set took the same time to fall.
2. Sample Answer: The soccer ball and the marble and the book and the pencil should take the same amount of time to fall. However, air resistance might affect some of the objects, and as air resistance increases, falling rate decreases.
3. Look for answers that include testing their prediction by holding two of the objects at the same height, releasing them at the same time, and observing whether or not they land at the same time.

Quick Lab

Orbiting Earth

Unlocking the Key Concept

This activity will help students understand how centripetal force causes an object to move in a curved path.

Inquiry Focus

Draw Conclusions—interpreting an observation to suggest that centripetal force causes curved motion

Group Size Pairs

Class Time 10 minutes

Advance Preparation

You may want to cut the cardboard/heavy paper into 5 cm × 60 cm strips.

Alternative Materials

Heavy paper may be used instead of cardboard, and any small ball may be used instead of the marble. Corrugated cardboard will not work because it crimps.

Safety

Students should wear safety goggles during this activity.

Procedure Tips

1. Caution students not to flick the marble too hard or it may fly out of the cardboard loop.
2. Sample Answer for Procedure Step 3: It will move in a straight line.

Answers

1. Sample Answer: The marble went around the loop in circles. Centripetal force from the cardboard ring pushing on it caused the marble to move this way.
2. Look for answers that mention inertia and its effect on the marble. Students will observe the marble moving straight because inertia carried it in a straight line.
3. Earth's gravity

Name ______________________ Date ____________ Class ____________

Inquiry Warm-Up

Is the Force With You?

Forces affect the way that objects move. In this activity, you will observe how equal and unequal forces affect the motion of an object.

INQUIRY FOCUS **Observe**

Procedure

1. Attach a spring scale to each end of the skateboard. Tie the string to the center of the axles if necessary.
2. Gently pull on one spring scale with a force of 4 N, while your partner pulls on the other with the same force. Observe the motion of the skateboard.
3. Next, gently pull on one spring scale, while your partner holds the other without pushing or pulling. Observe the motion of the skateboard and the readings on the spring scales.
4. Now try to keep your partner's spring scale at 2 N while you pull with a force of 4 N. Observe the motion of the skateboard.

Materials

skateboard

two 40-cm pieces of string

two spring scales

Think It Over

1. Describe the motion of the skateboard when you and your partner pulled with the same force.

____

____

2. What did you observe when you pulled on your spring scale but your partner just held the other spring scale?

____

____

3. How was the motion of the skateboard affected when you pulled with more force than your partner?

____

____

Name ______________________ Date ____________ Class ____________

Quick Lab

What Is Force?

A force is a push or a pull on an object. To describe a force, you need to tell how strong it is and in what direction it is exerted.

INQUIRY FOCUS **Infer**

Procedure

1. Hook two spring scales to the washer. Each partner should hold one spring scale.
2. Pull on your scales until you are each exerting a force of 10 N. You and your partner may need to experiment by pulling in different directions in order to accomplish this goal. **CAUTION:** ***Do not exert a force greater than 10 N on each spring scale.***
3. Read each scale. Compare the two readings.
4. Note the direction of the forces that you and your partner are exerting.
5. Note whether the washer is moving while both of you are pulling on it.
6. While remaining in the same pulling positions that you used in Step 2, have one partner try to decrease his or her force to 5 N, while the other continues to exert a force of 10 N.
7. Note whether the washer moves now.

Materials

20-N spring scales
large washer

Think It Over

1. In Step 2, how did the direction of your force compare with the direction of your partner's force?

____

____

2. Did the washer move when both partners exerted 10 N? Explain your result.

____

____

3. Did the washer move when one partner decreased the force he or she was exerting? Explain your result.

____

____

Name ______________________ Date ____________ Class ____________

Quick Lab

10 min 

Modeling Unbalanced Forces

Forces must act on an object for it to move. In this activity, you will perform a tug-of-war, observe the results, and describe the forces involved.

INQUIRY FOCUS **Make Models**

Procedure

Materials

rope, about 4 m long
masking tape

1. Place a piece of masking tape near the center of a length of rope. A team of students should stand on each side of the tape.
2. Have one classmate hold the rope where the masking tape is located.
3. The two teams should pick up their ends of the rope and pull just enough to remove any slack.
4. ⚠ On the count of three, the student holding the rope at the center lets it go and the two teams pull on the rope.
5. The student at the center of the rope uses the position of the tape to determine which team wins the tug-of-war.

Think It Over

1. Why was one team able to pull the rope to win the contest?

____

____

____

2. In what direction is the net force when one team is winning?

____

____

3. If one team causes the other team to move, what do you know about the forces of the teams?

____

____

____

Name ______________________________ Date______________ Class________________

Inquiry Warm-Up

Observing Friction

Friction is the force that two surfaces exert on each other when they rub together. In this activity, you will observe how friction affects the motion of an object. You will also explore how friction is affected by the surfaces involved.

INQUIRY FOCUS Observe

Procedure

Materials

2 sheets sandpaper
2 sheets wax paper
2 sheets notebook paper
small, heavy object

1. Place a sheet of wax paper on the surface of a clean table. Lightly rub your hand across the surface of the sheet and observe how it feels.
2. Place the other sheet of wax paper on top of the first so that the top sheet overlaps the bottom sheet on the end toward you. Then place the small, heavy object on top of the second sheet.
3. Hold the bottom sheet down to the table with one hand. Slowly pull on the edge of the top sheet. Observe how much force it takes to pull the top sheet across the bottom sheet.
4. Repeat Steps 1 through 3 using the other two types of paper.

Think It Over

1. Describe the texture of each type of paper.

____

____

____

2. Which type of paper required the most force to be moved? Which required the least?

____

____

3. How is the texture of a surface related to the friction that results when you slide it?

____

____

____

Name ______________________ Date__________ Class__________

Lab Investigation

PRE LAB

Sticky Sneakers

Reviewing Content

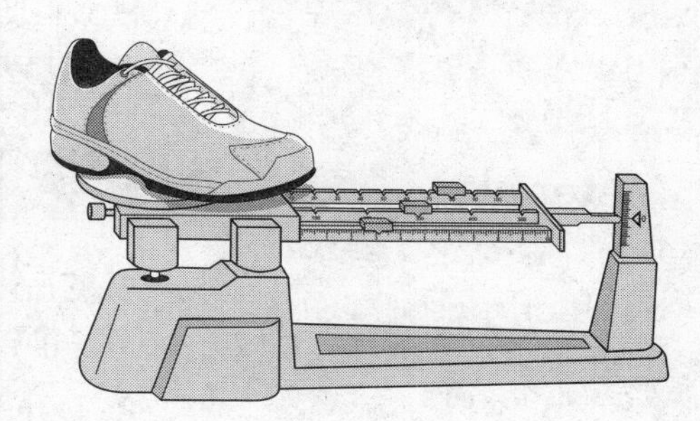

No surfaces are perfectly smooth. When two surfaces are in contact there is always some resistance to one surface sliding over another. This resistance is a force called friction. Two factors determine the amount of friction between two surfaces. One is the properties of the surface—what they are made of and how rough or smooth they are. The other factor is how much force is pressing the surfaces together. In order to compare the friction of various objects on a surface, it is important that the objects be pressed on the surface with equal force.

In this lab, you will test various brands of sneakers, making certain that the shoes you are using are of equal mass. Sneakers are designed to deal with various friction forces, such as:

- starting friction, which is involved when you start from a stopped position
- forward-stopping friction, which is involved when you come to a forward stop
- sideways-stopping friction, which is involved when you come to a sideways stop

Reviewing Inquiry Focus

When you interpret data, you analyze and draw conclusions from the data, including measurements and observations. Then you draw conclusions based only on the data you observed. If you make a hypothesis first, you should interpret whether or not your data supports the hypothesis. Your interpretation may show that you need to collect more data, different data, or change the experiment in some way. In science, you must limit your interpretations to the actual data collected and not make assumptions beyond the data observed.

With these statements in mind, preview the Lab Investigation. Then answer the questions in the spaces provided.

1. What quantities will you measure in the lab? What are the units you will use when you collect data?

____

____

2. You will measure the mass of the shoes. How will you know if the shoes have equal weight? Explain.

____

____

Name ______________________ Date ____________ Class ______________

DIRECTED Inquiry

Sticky Sneakers

Problem

INQUIRY FOCUS
Interpret Data

How does the amount of friction compare among different sneakers and surfaces?

Materials

three or more different brands of sneakers
two spring scales, 5-N and 20-N, or force sensors
mass set
masking tape
3 large paper clips
balance

Procedure

1. Choose three sneakers to test. Use a piece of masking tape to label them A, B, and C.
2. Use the data table to record each type of friction for each shoe.

Data Table

Sneaker	Starting Friction (N)	Sideways-Stopping Friction (N)	Forward-Stopping Friction (N)
A			
B			
C			

3. Place shoe A on the balance. Then place masses in the shoe so the total mass of the shoe plus the masses is 1000 g. Spread the masses out evenly inside the shoe.
4. Repeat Step 3 for shoes B and C.

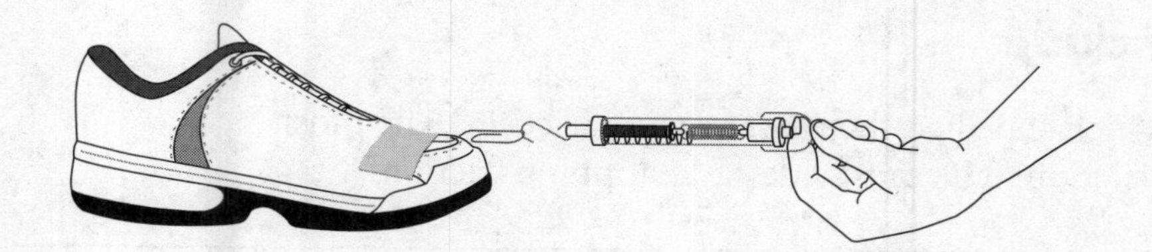

5. Tape a paper clip to each shoe and then attach a spring scale to the paper clip. Bend the paper clip as needed so that you can pull the shoe with the scale. (If you are using force sensors, see your teacher for instructions.)
   To measure:
   - starting friction, attach the paper clip to the back of the shoe.
   - forward-stopping friction, attach the paper clip to the front of the shoe.
   - sideways-stopping friction, attach the paper clip to the side of the shoe.
6. To measure starting friction, pull the shoe backward until it starts to move. Use the 20-N spring scale first. If the reading is less than 5 N, use the 5-N scale. The force necessary to make the shoe start moving is equal to the friction force. Record the starting friction force in your data table.
7. To measure both types of stopping friction, use the spring scale to pull each shoe at a slow, constant speed. Record the stopping friction forces in your data table.
8. Repeat Steps 5–7 for the remaining shoes.

Analyze and Conclude

1. **Interpret Data** Which shoe had the most starting friction? The most forward-stopping friction? The most sideways-stopping friction?

2. **Control Variables** What are the manipulated and responding variables in this experiment? Explain.

3. **Observe** Why is the reading on the spring scale equal to the force of friction in each case?

4. **Draw Conclusions** Do you think that comparing shoes with a small amount of mass in it is a fair test of the friction of the shoes? Explain.

5. **Infer** Why did you pull the shoe at a slow speed to test for stopping friction? Why did you pull a shoe that wasn't moving to test starting friction?

6. **Develop a Hypothesis** What is the relationship between the brand of sneaker and the amount of friction you observed? What do you observe that might cause one shoe to grip the floor better than another?

Name ______________________ Date ____________ Class ____________

DIRECTED Inquiry — Lab Investigation

POST LAB

Sticky Sneakers

1 **Design an Experiment** How could you modify your experiment so that the results compare the friction qualities of different sneakers more accurately and in more of a real-world way?

2 **Draw Conclusions** Tell how you can apply the results of this activity the next time you try on sneakers at a shoe store. Keep in mind that you cannot damage or cause wear to new shoes unless you buy them.

3 **Summarize** Describe what you learned about friction and the difference in the force of friction among different sneakers. List any questions you still have.

What I learned

What I still want to know

Communicate

Demonstrate Consumer Literacy Design an advertising brochure for a sneaker that you would wear for your favorite activity. Draw a diagram that shows the forces acting on the shoe for each type of motion. Tell why that shoe would be ideal for your favorite activity.

Name ______________________ Date ______________ Class ______________

OPEN Inquiry

Sticky Sneakers

Problem

How does the amount of friction compare among different sneakers and surfaces?

INQUIRY FOCUS
Control Variables, Predict, Interpret Data

Materials

various brands of sneakers

various types of surfaces

two spring scales, 5-N and 20-N, or force sensors

mass set(s)

3 large paper clips

balance

Design an Experiment

1. Imagine you are a sneaker designer. To design the best sneakers, you need to determine how friction affects your products and their performance. For example, if you are designing a basketball shoe, you might need a sole that is good at grabbing both the smooth wood floor of an indoor court and the rougher texture of an outdoor asphalt court.

2. Begin by deciding whether you will test how different sneakers react to friction on a single type of surface or you will test one type of sneaker and how it is affected by friction on multiple surfaces. Look at your materials. Which items do you think will work best for your experiment? Are there any materials that you don't need for your particular test?

3. Make a prediction based on the materials you've collected. Write your prediction on the lines below.

____

____

4. Design an experiment that will measure the force of friction between sneakers and surfaces. Write a procedure to include the materials you've collected. Determine which type(s) of friction you will test and how many trials you will run. Organize your results and observations on the following page. Consider these questions:

> **a.** Do you need to change how the spring scale is attached to the sneaker depending on what type of friction you are testing?
>
> **b.** Which spring scale should you use to get the most accurate results?
>
> **c.** If using multiple sneakers, what can you do to control the different masses of each sneaker?

5. Have your teacher review your hypothesis and procedure. Once approved, perform your tests and record your data.

Procedure

____

____

____

____

____

____

____

____

Data Table

Analyze and Conclude

1. **Control Variables** What factors influence the force of friction? How does the mass of the shoe affect these factors?

2. **Predict** Describe the results of your experiment and state whether or not they support your prediction.

3. **Interpret Data** Which shoe or surface had the greatest starting frictional force? Did the same shoe or surface also have the greatest stopping and sideways stopping friction? Explain.

4. **Design an Experiment** If you were a shoe designer, what would be your next step for testing the frictional forces of your sneakers' soles? How would you redesign the experiment for more realistic results?

Name ______________________ Date ____________ Class ____________

OPEN Inquiry — **Lab Investigation**

POST LAB

Sticky Sneakers

1 **Draw Conclusions** Athletic shoes worn on natural grass fields often have spikes or cleats. Why?

____

____

____

____

2 **Infer** Imagine you are a car tire manufacturer. Describe the characteristics your tires would need for starting and stopping in a wide variety of weather conditions.

____

____

____

____

3 **Summarize** Describe what you learned about friction and the difference in the force of friction among different sneakers. List any questions you still have.

What I learned

____

____

____

What I still want to know

____

____

____

Communicate

Demonstrate Consumer Literacy Use the data you collected from this experiment to design an advertising poster for a new basketball sneaker that your company is producing. Discuss the importance of:

- the different forces of friction on an indoor court and an outdoor court
- the effect of a person's mass on the performance of the sneaker's sole
- matching the right sneaker sole to the right sneaker usage

Name ______________________ Date ____________ Class ____________

Quick Lab

20 min 

Calculating

The weight in newtons of an object on Earth is the force that Earth's gravity exerts on the object. The amount of that force depends on the object's mass. In this activity, you will calculate weight after measuring mass.

INQUIRY FOCUS Measure

Procedure

1. Estimate the weight in newtons of each of the four objects. *Hint: A small lemon or a stick of butter weighs about 1 N.*
2. Use the balance to determine the mass of each object. If the measurements are in grams, convert them to kilograms.
3. Multiply each mass in kilograms by 9.8 m/s^2 to determine the weight in newtons. Compare the calculated weights with your estimated weights.
4. Exchange your objects with those from another group. Repeat Steps 1–3 to see if your estimates improve.

Materials

balance
four different objects

Think It Over

1. How close were your estimates to actual weights?

____

____

2. How do you explain any large errors in your estimates?

____

____

____

3. Did your estimates improve in Step 4? Explain.

____

____

____

Name ______________________ Date __________ Class __________

Inquiry Warm-Up

What Changes Motion?

A force is needed to change the motion of an object—to start it, stop it, speed it up, slow it down, or change its direction. You will observe what happens when a force stops a toy car, but no force acts on the load the car is carrying.

INQUIRY FOCUS Predict

Procedure

1. Stack several metal washers on top of the toy car.
2. Place a heavy book on the floor near the car.
3. Predict what will happen to both the car and the washers if you roll the car into the book.
4. Test your prediction and record your observations.

Materials

toy car
5 washers
heavy book

Think It Over

1. What happened to the car when it hit the book?

____

____

2. What happened to the washers when the car hit the book?

____

____

3. What might be the reason for any difference between the motions of the car and the washers?

____

____

____

Name ______________________ Date ____________ Class ____________

Quick Lab — 15 min

Around and Around

Newton's first law is also called the law of inertia. All objects have inertia. This means that moving objects stay in motion and objects at rest stay at rest, unless acted upon by a force.

INQUIRY FOCUS Infer

Procedure

1. Tape one end of a length of string (about 1 m) to a table tennis ball.
2. Suspend the ball in front of you and swing it clockwise in a horizontal circle, keeping it 2–3 cm above the floor. **CAUTION: *Keep the ball near the floor while swinging it.***
3. Let go of the string and observe the direction in which the ball rolls.
4. Repeat this several times, letting go of the string at different points.

Materials

table tennis ball
string, 1 m
tape

Think It Over

1. At what point do you need to let go of the string if you want the ball to roll directly away from you?

____

____

2. At what point do you need to let go of the string if you want the ball to roll directly toward you?

____

____

3. The string exerts a force on the ball so that it keeps moving in a circle. Write a sentence describing what happens to the motion of the ball when you release the string.

____

____

Name ______________________ Date __________ Class __________

Quick Lab

Newton's Second Law

Acceleration is the rate at which velocity changes. Newton's second law says that acceleration depends on the mass of an object being moved and the amount of force acting on the object.

INQUIRY FOCUS Infer

Procedure

1. Tape the string firmly to the roof of the toy car. Pull on the string to make sure that you can pull the car along the table without the string coming loose. Position the car at one end of your table.
2. Bend the paper clip to make a hook on which you can hang the washers.
3. Drape the string over the edge of the far end of your worktable and tie the hook to the string so that it hangs about 10 cm below the table edge.
4. Hang just enough washers on the hook to cause the car to barely begin to move along the table.
5. Move the car back to the starting position. Hold the car still and add 3 more washers to the hook. Release the car. Note any differences in its motion.

Materials

toy car
masking tape
string
large paper clip
medium-sized washers

Think It Over

1. What force was overcome when you added just enough washers to move the car?

____

____

2. In terms of acceleration, how was the motion of the car in Step 5 different from that in Step 4?

____

____

3. How can you explain the difference in acceleration between Steps 4 and 5?

____

____

____

Name ______________________ Date ____________ Class ____________

Quick Lab

20 min 

Interpreting Illustrations

Newton's third law says that any time a force is exerted on an object, the object exerts an equal force in the opposite direction. In this activity, you will find and examine illustrations of this law and identify the forces involved.

INQUIRY FOCUS **Make Models**

Procedure

1. Search magazines to find pictures that illustrate motion and action.
2. Look for examples that illustrate pairs of action and reaction forces.
3. Cut out the examples and glue them to the poster board.
4. Use markers to label the forces illustrated in the clippings.

Materials

magazines
scissors
glue
markers
poster board

Think It Over

1. Choose one of the examples you found and describe the pair of action and reaction forces illustrated.

____

____

____

____

2. Suppose you are walking on a concrete surface and suddenly slip as you step on a patch of ice. How do the pairs of action and reaction forces differ when you are on the dry walk and when you step on the ice?

____

____

____

____

Name ______________________ Date______________ Class______________

Inquiry Warm-Up

How Pushy Is a Straw?

What happens if you push on an automobile and on a toy car with the same force? In this activity, you will observe how the same amount of force affects the motion of different objects.

INQUIRY FOCUS **Develop a Hypothesis**

Procedure

Materials

- hard cover book
- rubber band
- marbles
- plastic straw

1. Stretch a rubber band around the middle of the cover of the hardcover book.
2. Place four marbles in a small square on a table. Place the book on the marbles so that the cover with the rubber band is on top.
3. Hold the book steady by placing one index finger on the binding. Then, as shown, push a straw against the rubber band with your other index finger. The edge of the straw should dig into the rubber band.

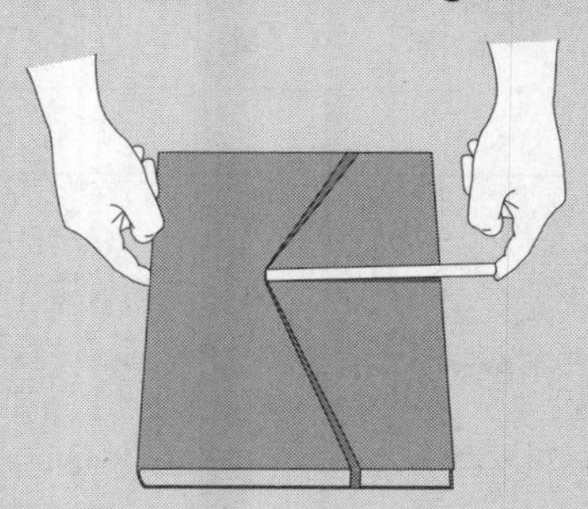

4. Push the straw until the rubber band stretches about 10 cm. Then let go of both the book and the straw at the same time.

Think It Over

1. Compare the speeds and directions of the straw and the book after you let go.

____

____

2. Suppose you repeated the experiment, but instead of a straw you used an object with a mass very close to the mass of the book. Predict how the final speeds of the objects would compare. Develop a hypothesis that would explain the relationship between the objects' masses and their final speeds.

____

____

Name ______________________ Date ____________ Class ____________

Quick Lab — 10 min

Colliding Cars

Momentum is always conserved—even by toys. In this activity, you will produce collisions between toy cars to observe how momentum is conserved and then predict the outcome of other collisions.

INQUIRY FOCUS **Predict**

Procedure

Materials
masking tape
two toy cars

1. Find two nearly identical toy cars that roll easily.
2. Make two loops out of masking tape (sticky side out). Put one loop on the front of one of the cars and the other loop on the back of the other car.
3. Place the car that has tape on its back on the floor. Then gently roll the other car into the back of the stationary car. Observe what happens.
4. Predict what will happen if you put masking tape on the fronts of both cars and roll them at each other with equal speeds. Test your prediction.

____

____

Think It Over

1. What happened when you rolled the car into the back of the stationary car?

____

____

____

2. Did your test confirm your prediction?

____

____

____

3. Was momentum conserved? How do you know?

____

____

____

Name ______________________ Date ____________ Class ____________

Inquiry Warm-Up

What Makes an Object Move in a Circle?

Gravitational force causes objects to fall to Earth, but it is also one of the forces that causes satellites to orbit around Earth. In this activity, you will observe how a force causes an object to move in a circle.

INQUIRY FOCUS Infer

Procedure

1. Tie an empty thread spool to the end of the string.
2. Swing the spool rapidly around in a circle that is perpendicular to the floor. **CAUTION:** ***Make sure no one is near the swinging spool, and don't let it go!***
3. Increase the speed of the spool slightly and then return to your original speed. Observe what you feel from the string while doing this.
4. Predict what will happen if you decrease the speed of the spool. Test your prediction.

Materials

80–90-cm length of string
empty thread spool

Think It Over

1. What did you observe when you swung the spool faster?

____

____

2. What did you predict would happen in Step 4? Was your prediction correct or incorrect?

____

____

____

3. An object moving in a circular path is accelerating because it is changing direction. What caused the spool to accelerate? How do you know?

____

____

____

Name ______________________ Date __________ Class __________

Quick Lab

Which Lands First?

In this activity, you will observe the time required for objects of different masses to fall due to the force of gravity. Then you will use what you observed to describe how other objects will behave when they are in free fall.

INQUIRY FOCUS Design an Experiment

Procedure

1. Tape three quarters together in a stack. Make sure the tape is wrapped tightly around them and the quarters are held firmly together.
2. Place the stack of quarters next to a single quarter near the edge of your desk.
3. Lay the ruler on the desk behind the coins. Line it up parallel to the edge of the desk and just touching the coins.
4. Keeping the ruler parallel to the edge of the desk, use it to push the coins over the edge at the same time. Observe how long the coins take to land. Repeat to confirm your results.

Materials

4 quarters
ruler
tape

Think It Over

1. Did you see a difference in the time it took the coins to fall? Explain.

____

____

2. Use what you observed to predict whether a soccer ball will fall more quickly than a marble. Will a pencil fall more quickly than a book? What factors could affect the amount of time it takes an object to fall?

____

____

____

3. How can you test your predictions?

____

____

____

Name ______________________ Date__________ Class__________

Quick Lab

10 min

Orbiting Earth

In this activity, you will explore circular motion and centripetal force. You will use your observations to infer how satellites move around Earth.

INQUIRY FOCUS Draw Conclusions

Procedure

1. Form the cardboard strip into a loop and tape the ends together. Place the open side of the loop flat on your desk.
2. Place the marble next to the inside wall of the cardboard loop. Flick the marble so that it rolls along the inside of the loop. Observe how the marble moves.
3. How do you think the marble will move if you flick it and then remove the loop while it is rolling?

____

____

4. Flick the marble and remove the loop to find out.

Materials

marble

5 cm × 60 cm cardboard strip

masking tape

Think It Over

1. How did the marble move the first time you flicked it? What force made it move this way?

____

____

2. How did the marble move when you removed the cardboard loop? Why?

____

____

3. Imagine the marble is a satellite orbiting Earth. What force does the cardboard loop represent?

____

____

CHAPTER 3

TABLE OF CONTENTS

Work and Machines

Teacher Notes 65

Work and Power

Inquiry Warm-Up	Pulling at an Angle	70
Quick Lab	What Is Work?	71
Quick Lab	Investigating Power	72

Understanding Machines

Inquiry Warm-Up	Is It a Machine?	73
Quick Lab	Going Up	74
Quick Lab	Mechanical Advantage	75
Quick Lab	Friction and Efficiency	76

Inclined Planes and Levers

Inquiry Warm-Up	Inclined Planes and Levers		77
Lab Investigation	Angling for Access	*Pre Lab*	78
		Directed Inquiry	79
		Open Inquiry	83
Quick Lab	Modeling Levers		87

Putting Machines Together

Inquiry Warm-Up	Machines That Turn	88
Quick Lab	Building Pulleys	89
Quick Lab	Machines in the Kitchen	90

Work and Power

Answering the Big Question

The activities in this lesson will help students answer the Big Question by having them hypothesize about the effect of the angle of applied force on the ease of moving an object and by allowing them to explore the concepts of work and power and learn how to calculate the amount of work and power involved in moving an object.

Inquiry Warm-Up

Pulling at an Angle

Inquiry Focus

Develop a Hypothesis—using prior knowledge or experience to state the expected relationship between the angle of an applied force and how easily an object moves

Group Size Groups

Class Time 10 minutes

Materials

Mugs with straight sides or with a diameter larger at the bottom than at the top are best for the activity. Mugs with a top diameter larger than the bottom diameter should be avoided.

Procedure Tips

1. Students should fill the mug halfway to prevent it from turning over when pulled.
2. Have students place the elastic close to the bottom of the handle to reduce the possibility of tipping the mug.
3. Provide paper towels to clean up any spills.
4. Sample Hypothesis for Procedure Step 4: Less force is needed to move the mug when the elastic halves are held parallel.

Answers

1. The elastic stretches more when pulling with the elastic halves held in parallel to each other than when pulling with the elastic halves held at an angle to each other.
2. Pulling with the elastic halves held at an angle to each other required more force to move the mug. When holding the elastic halves at an angle to each other, more force is used to stretch the elastic sideways than to move the mug.

Quick Lab

What Is Work?

Unlocking the Key Concept

This activity will help students calculate the amount of work they do moving an object and distinguish between instances in which work is and is not done.

Inquiry Focus

Measure—collecting data using spring scales and meter sticks

Group Size Groups

Class Time 20 minutes

Safety

1. To avoid possible injury, remind students that the meter sticks are to be used for measuring only.
2. Gravel on the floor could present a slipping hazard. Remind students to pick up any gravel that might fall to the floor.

Advance Preparation (5 minutes)

Organize materials at lab stations for each group. Each group should have a sandwich bag of the gravel. Alternatively, you may choose to pre-fill a can with gravel for each group before class.

Alternative Materials

Students can use any sturdy object. The soda can is suggested because the mass can be varied and it has a tab, which can be used as a convenient lifting point.

Procedure Tips

1. Be sure the tabs on the soda cans are firmly attached and secure. Remind students to express weights and forces in newtons, distance in meters, and work in joules.
2. If the spring scales are calibrated in kilograms, students should multiply the reading by 9.8 to obtain newtons.

Answers

1. Sample Answer: If the weight is 4.0 N and the tabletop is 0.70 m from the floor, work = 4.0 N × 0.70 m = 2.8 joules.
2. In Step 4, I pulled the can up, and the can moved up. In Step 5, I pulled the can up, but the can moved forward horizontally as I walked.

3. no, because the direction of the force (up) was not the same as the direction the can moved (horizontally)

Quick Lab

Investigating Power

Unlocking the Key Concept

This activity will help students explore how doing the same amount of work at different speeds affects the amount of power used.

Inquiry Focus

Calculate—using mathematical processes to determine how much work and power are involved in lifting an object

Group Size Groups

Class Time 20 minutes

Alternative Materials

Any objects of moderate weight can be used. Objects should be heavy enough that students can feel the difference in the amount of power employed when they lift the objects rapidly compared to lifting them slowly. The objects chosen should be sturdy enough that they are not damaged if students drop them. Also, the objects should not be so heavy that they can fall and harm students.

Procedure Tips

1. Have one student hold a meter stick vertically on the table, so that the student lifting the weight can raise it to a uniform height.
2. As a challenge, have students measure the total time in each of Steps 1 and 2, and calculate the ratio of power between the two steps.

Answers

1. The amount of work done was the same regardless of the amount of time used.
2. time
3. Look for answers that multiply the force from Step 1 by the distance the object was lifted. Since the distance was the same for both trials, the two amounts of work should be equal.
4. Look for answers that divide the amount of work by the time in each trial. Students' calculations should show a greater power for the second trial.
5. Look for answers that refer to Step 3 of the procedure. Since power is the rate of work, more power is used when work is done faster.

Understanding Machines

Answering the Big Question

The activities in this lesson will help students answer the Big Question by having them create their own working definition of a machine, investigate factors that affect mechanical advantage, and use simple machines to investigate the effects of friction on the efficiency of a machine.

Inquiry Warm-Up

Is It a Machine?

Inquiry Focus

Form an Operational Definition—creating a definition of the term *machine* by observing various objects and classifying them based on an understanding of the characteristics that define an object as a machine

Group Size Groups

Class Time 20 minutes

Materials

1. Objects that are machines include the following: cheese grater, corkscrew, pliers, screwdriver, wrench, pry bar, fishing rod, flyswatter, door knob.
2. Objects that are not machines include the following: ball, book, chalk, eraser, paper, pencil, ruler, cardboard box.

Advance Preparation

Make sure to supply objects that have clear functions. Each object should function either only as a machine or not as a machine.

Procedure Tips

1. Give each group a few objects to examine.
2. Once a group has classified an object, the students should pass it to another group.
3. Allow students to classify machines based on their own criteria.

Answers

1. Look for answers that explain how to classify an item as a machine by giving characteristics of machines.

2. Sample Answer: A flathead screwdriver is a wedge. When used to pry open a can, the wedge increases the output force by increasing the distance in which the input force is applied. A fishing rod is a pulley that changes the direction of the applied force. A bottle opener is a lever that increases the output force and changes the direction of the force.

Quick Lab

Going Up

Unlocking the Key Concept

This activity will help students observe how friction affects the amount of force needed to lift a stationary object.

Inquiry Focus

Develop a Hypothesis—using prior knowledge or experience to make a statement about how friction will affect the force required to lift a stationary object

Group Size Groups

Class Time 15 minutes

Advance Preparation

Make sure that objects have a mass of about 500 g and a handle that allows the string to be easily attached to the object.

Alternative Materials

Large drinking mugs and small frying pans (18-cm diameter) can be used. The objects should be sturdy enough that they will not be damaged if students drop them.

Procedure Tips

1. Students should read the spring scale while the pot is moving rather than when they are just pulling on the string.
2. Help students analyze results by asking them to compare the amount of friction on the string in Steps 3 and 4.
3. Sample Hypothesis for Procedure Step 1: More force is needed to lift the pot when the string is rubbing against the pencil.

Answers

1. Sample Answer: The readings confirmed my hypothesis. The reading for the string looped over the pencil was higher.
2. Friction between the string and the pencil increased the amount of force needed to lift the pot, which in turn caused the higher reading.
3. In some situations, pulling down may be easier than pulling up.

Quick Lab

Mechanical Advantage

Unlocking the Key Concept

This activity will help students understand the relationship between mechanical advantage and the ratio of output force to input force. Students will demonstrate that for a given output force, a longer input lever arm produces a greater output force and requires less input force than a shorter input lever.

Inquiry Focus

Draw Conclusions—analyzing two different versions of a machine doing work to make a statement about factors that affect mechanical advantage

Group Size Groups

Class Time 15 minutes

Alternative Materials

A large book (about 2-cm thick), non-corrugated cardboard, and a yardstick can be used.

Procedure Tips

1. A smooth stack of papers works best for this procedure. If the stack is loose or uneven, the papers may tear rather than lift from the desktop.
2. Students should adjust the length of the meter stick under the stack of papers to prevent spontaneous lifting.

Answers

1. a lever
2. The meter stick had the greater mechanical advantage. The papers were easier to lift using it.
3. The meter stick had a greater output force compared to the ruler.

Quick Lab

Friction and Efficiency

 Unlocking the Key Concept

This activity will help students investigate how friction affects the amount of force required to do work. They will determine that as the friction in a pair of scissors increases, the tension between the blades increases, which results in a lower efficiency.

Inquiry Focus

Classify—ordering pairs of scissors from most efficient to least efficient

Group Size Large groups (6–7 students)

Class Time 10 minutes

Safety

To avoid cuts and other injuries, remind students to use care when operating scissors or the related alternative cutting devices. Remind students to always direct a sharp edge or point away from themselves and others.

Alternative Materials

Garden shears, thin cardboard, and metal snips can be used.

Procedure Tips

1. Obtain scissors with an adjustable tension screw. Sewing centers often sell this type of scissors.
2. Small garden shears with adjustable tension also are acceptable, but make sure they will cut paper.

Answers

1. Look for answers that give examples of categories for classifying scissors, such as blade length, blade shape, or handle size.
2. Efficient scissors require less input force to cut paper.
3. Increasing the friction in a pair of scissors increases the input force needed to do work.

Inclined Planes and Levers

 Answering the Big Question

The activities in this lesson will help students answer the Big Question by allowing them to model levers and inclined planes and explore how levers and inclined planes function as simple machines that make work easier.

Inquiry Warm-Up

Inclined Planes and Levers

Inquiry Focus

Observe—using senses to gather information; gathering and recording data; using force measurements to see how a lever and an inclined plane affects the force needed to lift a weight

Group Size Groups

Class Time 15 minutes

Safety

1. Students should make sure the weight is never too close to the end of the table.
2. Tell students to pull slowly on the spring scale to avoid flipping the weight and potentially breaking the ruler.
3. Students should wear safety goggles during this lab.

Advance Preparation

1. The spring scale used should be able to measure a minimum of 10 N.
2. Use square knots to tie the string into loops before the lab. Students might not know how to tie a stable knot.
3. Distribute materials at lab stations for each group.

Alternative Materials

A wooden paint stirrer can be used instead of the ruler. Mark cm increments on the stirrer.

Procedure Tips

1. With a 0.5-kg weight, the force that students measure in Step 1 will be about 5 N.
2. Hexagonal pencils work best because they don't roll as easily as round pencils.

Answers

1. The force was either greater or smaller than in Step 1, depending on where it was applied. The force required is greater if it is applied closer to the fulcrum. The force required is smaller if it is applied farther from the fulcrum. The force required is smallest at the end of the ruler.
2. Pushing up the ramp would require less force; both inclined planes and levers reduce the amount of input force by allowing you to spread the input force over a longer distance.

Lab Investigation

Angling for Access

 Unlocking the Key Concept

Both Versions This activity will help students illustrate that the actual and ideal mechanical advantages of an inclined plane vary with its steepness.

Answers—Pre Lab

Both Versions:

1. Students will need to measure the weight to be lifted (the block), the force needed to slide the block up the ramp, the effective length of the ramp, and the height of the raised end of the ramp. Weight and force will be measured in newtons. Length and height will be measured in centimeters.
2. Because of the effect of friction, the AMA will always be less than the IMA.

Answers—Do the Math

$\text{IMA} = \frac{60 \text{ cm}}{8 \text{ cm}} = 7.5$

Inquiry Focus

Both Versions:

Interpret Data—analyzing and drawing conclusions from data students collect by testing their own models of wheelchair ramps

Group Size

Both Versions Large groups (6–7 students)

Class Time

Directed Inquiry 30 minutes

Open Inquiry 60 minutes

Advance Preparation (20 minutes)

Directed Inquiry:

If using a dynamics cart, the weight of the cart should be within the capacity of the spring scales available. Add objects to the cart to increase weight.

Alternative Materials

Directed Inquiry:

A dynamics cart can be substituted for the wooden block.

Open Inquiry:

Graph paper, blocks, and sturdy cardboard can be used.

Procedure Tips

Directed Inquiry:

1. You may wish to have students brainstorm ways in which they could model a ramp using the displayed materials. Ask, **What variables can you manipulate?** *(weight of block, steepness of ramp, type of material ramp is made of, length of ramp)* **What are some responding variables?** *(force needed to pull the block up the ramp, amount of friction)*
2. Show students how to use and zero a spring scale. Remind students to pull the spring scale parallel to the inclined plane to prevent inaccurate readings. If the spring scale is calibrated in grams, have students multiply by 0.01 to get an approximate reading in newtons.
3. Make sure students measure the distance from the tabletop to the bottom (not the top) of the board at the edge mark to get their measurement of the ramp's height. Otherwise, they are likely to measure to the top of the board, which will be incorrect.
4. The block or cart should be pulled at a slow, constant speed to measure the pulling force. Remind students not to read the scale until the block or cart is moving smoothly at a constant speed. The force needed to get the block or cart moving will be more than this and should not be used.
5. Expected Outcome: The actual mechanical advantage will always be less than the ideal mechanical advantage. The actual mechanical advantage decreases with increased height. If both cart and block are used, the actual mechanical advantage for the cart will be much higher than for the block.

6. Sample Hypothesis for Procedure Step 1: The force needed to push a wheelchair up a low-angle ramp is less than what is needed to push a chair up a high-angle ramp.

Open Inquiry:

1. Make sure students measure the distance from the tabletop to the bottom (not the top) of the board at the edge mark when measuring the ramp's height. Otherwise, they are likely to measure to the top of the board, which will be incorrect.
2. If the spring scale is calibrated in grams, students should multiply by 0.01 to obtain an approximate reading in newtons.
3. The block or cart should be pulled at a slow, constant speed to measure the pulling force. Remind students to avoid reading the scale until the block or cart is moving smoothly at a constant speed. The force needed to get the block or cart moving will be more than this and should not be used.
4. Make sure students understand their goals for the activity (outlined in Procedure Step 1).
5. Sample Answer for Procedure Step 1a: The ramp needs to be 24 m long.
6. Sample Answers to Procedure Step 4:
   a. The wooden board and books can be used to build the ramp. If boards and books are not available, the following items can be used as alternative materials: assorted wooden blocks (2 cm × 10 cm, 4 cm × 10 cm, and 6 cm × 10 cm) and a shoebox lid or sturdy piece of cardboard (approximately 10 cm × 50 cm).
   b. The wooden cart (and additional weight, if necessary) can be used to represent the wheelchair.
   c. Students could set up a ramp with an ideal mechanical advantage of 12. The length to height ratio will need to be 12:1. Actual ramps will vary depending on the length of the wooden board. If students cannot set up this exact ratio, they should get as close as possible.
   d. The actual mechanical advantage can be determined by dividing the weight of the wooden cart by the force required to pull it up the ramp.
   e. Students should record data on the height and length of the ramp, weight of the cart, force required to pull the cart, ideal mechanical advantage, and actual mechanical advantage.
7. Accept all student predications in Step 6. However, the actual mechanical advantage should be less than the ideal.
8. Sample Answer to Procedure Step 9: The length of the ramp will need to be longer than 24 meters. To find the actual length, students will need to use the height and length of their scale model (the one that gave them an AMA > 12), and the height of the doorway (2 m) to find the length of the ramp. For example: If the height of the scale model is 3 cm and the length is 48 cm, and the height of the doorway is 200 cm (2 m), then

$$\frac{48 \text{ cm}}{3 \text{ cm}} = \frac{x \text{ (length of ramp)}}{200 \text{ cm}}$$

   and x = 3,200 cm or 32 meters
9. Students should realize that the actual ramp will not fit in the area in front of the building, so they will have to zig-zag the ramp in order for it to fit. Drawing a scale model may be difficult for some students. Consider allowing them to use graph paper to accomplish this task.

Answers—Analyze and Conclude

Directed Inquiry:

1. Sample Answer: The ideal mechanical advantage was always more than the actual mechanical advantage because friction exists between the block and the incline. The actual mechanical advantage is more helpful in determining the best ramp height because there will also be some friction between a wheelchair and the ramp. The ideal mechanical advantage assumes no friction.
2. As the height of the ramp increases, the ideal and actual mechanical advantages both decrease.
3. The best ramp should be one that gives the greatest actual mechanical advantage.
4. Look for answers that include an explanation of how the model helped to find a solution to the problem as well as ways the model did not accurately represent an actual wheelchair ramp and wheelchair.

5. Varying the length of the ramp would also affect the mechanical advantage.

Open Inquiry:

1. The IMA and AMA both decrease with increasing height if length is held constant. The IMA and AMA both increase with increasing length if height is held constant.
2. The model helped to collect data to determine how the actual mechanical advantage of the ramp compares to the ideal mechanical advantage. This allowed us to determine how long the actual ramp would need to be to have an actual mechanical advantage of 12. The model has limitations. For example, the wooden cart and wheelchair may have different amounts of friction, which would change the actual mechanical advantage.
3. Students should suggest building a prototype or full-size model of the ramp and testing it with an actual wheelchair.
4. Sample Answer: If the ramp had an AMA of 24, it would be easier to push the wheelchair up the ramp. However, it would be impractical because the ramp would have to be so long and gradual to achieve this AMA.
5. The actual mechanical advantage would be much less when the ramp is used for sliding the cartons than it would be for a wheelchair. Sliding friction is usually much greater than rolling friction. The increased force needed reduces the actual mechanical advantage of the ramp.

Answers—Post Lab

Directed Inquiry:

1. Sample Answer: I could replace the force needed to pull a sliding object with the force needed to pull a rolling object. In addition, I could do multiple trials of each ramp height and average the results.
2. Look for answers that give suggestions for designs that will fit in the available space, such as a zig-zag series of ramps or a ramp that is a continuous spiral.
3. Sample Answer: I learned that a steeper ramp gives a lower IMA as well as a lower AMA. The AMA is always lower than the IMA. I would like to find out how ramp slope affects the IMA and AMA when the object is moved by rolling rather than sliding.

Communicate—Different groups might reach the same conclusion, but some data in the individual trials might differ due to errors made when calculating the results.

Open Inquiry:

1. Look for answers that explain the parts of the lab that could go wrong or ways that the results could be inaccurate. Answers should also explain practical ways to keep these errors to a minimum, such as performing multiple trials.
2. The lower actual mechanical advantage of the full-size model indicates that there is more friction between the wheelchair and the ramp than there is between the wooden cart and the model ramp. In order to meet the ADA guidelines, the length of the ramp needs to be increased.
3. Students should express the idea that a steeper ramp gives a lower IMA as well as a lower AMA. They should note that the AMA is always lower than the IMA. They may have questions about how a scientist designing a ramp would actually carry out the testing and design process.

Communicate—Students' letters should demonstrate an understanding of the procedure involved in designing a ramp.

Quick Lab

Modeling Levers

Unlocking the Key Concept

This activity will help students demonstrate how the location of the fulcrum affects the location, magnitude, and direction of the input and output forces.

Inquiry Focus

Make Models—creating physical representations of the three types of levers, and then identifying the location of the input force, output force, and fulcrum on each

Group Size Pairs

Class Time 10 minutes

Alternative Materials

A ruler, pencil, and coin can be used.

Procedure Tips

Review the definition of the three classes of levers before the activity begins.

Answers

1. The force pressing down on the handle is the input force, the force lifting the bean is the output force, and the finger is the fulcrum. This is a first-class lever.
2. The force lifting the spoon handle is the input force, the force lifting the bean is the output force, and the bowl of the spoon is the fulcrum. This is a second-class lever.
3. Sample Answer: The input force is in the middle of the spoon handle, the output force is at the bowl of the spoon, and the fulcrum is at the top of the spoon handle.

Putting Machines Together

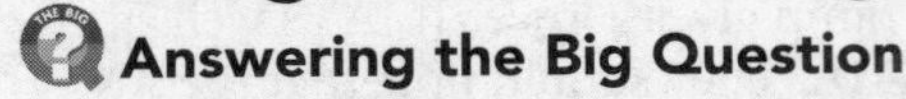

Answering the Big Question

The activities in this lesson will help students answer the Big Question by allowing them to investigate how wheel and axle assemblies and pulleys function as simple machines that make work easier. Students will also explore how simple and compound machines used in a kitchen make work easier.

Inquiry Warm-Up

Machines That Turn

Inquiry Focus

Observe—gathering information about how the force needed to turn a wheel compares to the force needed to turn an axle in a wheel and axle

Group Size Groups

Class Time 15 minutes

Materials

1. Use a 1-hole rubber stopper, No. 10.
2. Use a dowel that is 10 cm long ($\frac{3}{16}$ inch).

Alternative Materials

The rubber stopper can be any size, No. 7 or larger, as long as the hole is 5 mm. A large bolt can be used instead of the dowel, as long as the bolt fits snuggly into the hole in the stopper.

Procedure Tips

Make sure the dowel is held firmly in the stopper so that it does not slip when the students try to turn the dowel. You may wish to supply students with stoppers that have the dowel already inserted.

Answers

1. Turning the axle took much more effort than turning the wheel.
2. When you use a wheel and axle, you apply a low input force over a large distance. The result is that the axle produces a large output force over a small distance. This means you are able to turn the axle by turning the wheel with less force than if you tried to turn the axle alone.
3. Students should infer that the door of a bank vault has a much larger latching mechanism that requires much more force to open than an ordinary door. Thus, a much larger wheel is needed in order to lower the input force required.

Quick Lab

Building Pulleys

Unlocking the Key Concept

This activity will help students model how a pulley decreases the amount of work needed to lift an object. They will determine the mechanical advantage of a simple pulley system.

Inquiry Focus

Make Models—creating physical representations of the three basic types of pulleys to determine the mechanical advantage of each, and to measure the amount of force required by each to lift a weight

Group Size Groups

Class Time 15 minutes

Alternative Materials

Almost anything with a mass of about 1 kg can be used provided a cord can be easily attached to it.

Procedure Tips

1. A 1-kg mass has a weight of 9.8 N, so 20-N spring scales would work.

2. Review the types with students before starting the activity. Refer to the figure in the student edition that shows the three types of pulleys. Point out the location of the pulley(s) in each type of pulley system.
3. Remind students that they should read the spring scale while they are lifting the mass at a constant speed.

Answers

1. Look for answers that list the three types of pulleys constructed along with the force (in newtons) required to lift the mass using each pulley.
2. The ideal mechanical advantage in the fixed pulley is 1; in the movable pulley, it is 2; and in the block and tackle it is 3.
3. The direction of the force changed in the fixed pulley setup.

Quick Lab

Machines in the Kitchen

Unlocking the Key Concept

This activity will help students explore simple and compound machines found in a kitchen, thereby furthering their understanding of what constitutes a machine.

Inquiry Focus

Classify—putting kitchen tools into categories based on the type of machine they represent: simple or compound

Group Size Pairs

Class Time 10 minutes

Safety

1. To avoid possible injury, remind students to take care when handling objects that have points or sharp edges or ones that open and close.
2. Long hair should be tied back when using objects with moveable parts, such as an egg beater or can opener.

Advance Preparation

Plan ahead to make sure you'll have time to gather enough utensils.

Alternative Materials

You may substitute non-kitchen tools such as a hammer, screwdriver, hand-powered rotary drill, pliers, chisel, brace and bit, wrench, metal snips, bicycle, rake, hoe, grass shears, pruning shears, spade, paint brush, can crusher, C-clamp, or paint stirrer.

Procedure Tips

Make sure items with the potential to cause injury are available for examination only at a teacher-supervised station.

Answers

1. Sample Answer: The knife is a wedge that increases the output force. The cooking spoon is used as a lever in multiple ways. The bottle opener is a lever that increases force and changes direction of force.
2. Look for answers that list two compound machines and the simple machines found within each. Answers should include an explanation of how each compound machine makes work easier—by increasing output force or changing the direction of the force.
3. Sample Answer: A screwdriver is a wheel and axle, but often is used as a first-class lever when removing the lid from a paint can.

Name ______________________ Date ______________ Class ______________

Inquiry Warm-Up

10 min

Pulling at an Angle

How does the angle at which a force is applied to an object affect how easily the object is moved? In this activity, you will develop a hypothesis relating the angle of an applied force to how easily an object is moved.

INQUIRY FOCUS Develop a Hypothesis

Procedure

Materials

mug
medium-weight rubber band
water

1. Fill a mug half full with water.
2. Cut a medium-weight rubber band to make a strand of elastic. Thread the elastic through the mug handle.
3. You can hold the two halves of the elastic parallel to each other or at a horizontal angle to each other. (For example, hold the elastic halves parallel to each other. Then, move your left hand slightly to the left and move your right hand slightly to the right, without moving your hands up or down. The elastic halves should no longer be parallel to each other, but should now create close to a 90° angle when looking down on the elastic.) By pulling on the elastic, you can move the mug across the table.
4. Predict which method (parallel or at an angle) would be more effective in moving the mug. Use your prediction to develop a hypothesis relating the angle of a force to the ability to move an object.

____

____

5. Test your hypothesis by pulling on the elastic in both ways—with the elastic halves held parallel to each other and with the elastic halves held at an angle to each other.

Think It Over

1. How did the elastic stretch during each pull?

____

____

____

2. Which method required more force to move the mug? Explain your answer.

____

____

Name ______________________ Date__________ Class__________

Quick Lab

What Is Work?

You can push or pull on an object, but you are not doing work unless the object moves in the same direction as the push or pull. Work is calculated by multiplying the amount of force by the distance over which the force acts.

INQUIRY FOCUS **Measure**

Procedure

1. Use a funnel to put gravel into the soda can until the can is about half full. Thread the string through the tab of the can and tie the ends together to make a loop.
2. Use the spring scale to determine the force it takes to lift the can. Record the force in newtons. __________
3. Use the meter stick to measure the distance from the floor to the tabletop. Record your measurement in meters. __________
4. Place the can on the floor and lift it until the bottom edge meets the tabletop.
5. Use the tape to mark a two-meter distance on the floor. Walk two meters while carrying the can.

Materials

plastic funnel
soda can with tab
spring scale
string, 40 cm
small gravel
meter stick
masking tape

Think It Over

1. Calculate the amount of work you did in Step 4.

____

____

2. In which direction did you pull on the can in Step 4? In which direction did the can move? In which direction did you pull on the can in Step 5? In which direction did the can move?

____

____

3. Did you do work in Step 5? Explain.

____

____

Name ______________________ Date ______________ Class ______________

Quick Lab

Investigating Power

Power is the amount of work done in a unit of time. In this activity, you will compare the power you use in lifting different objects at different speeds.

INQUIRY FOCUS **Calculate**

Procedure

1. Use the spring scale to determine the force it takes to lift the object. Record the force in newtons. __________
2. Slowly lift the object you were given from the table-top to a height of 0.5 m. Repeat five times without stopping. Record your time in seconds. __________
3. Repeat Step 2, but lift the object quickly. Record your time in seconds. __________

Materials

various objects that can be comfortably lifted, such as small barbells or large cans of fruits or vegetables

meter stick

stopwatch

spring scale

Think It Over

1. Did you do more work on the object when you lifted it slowly or when you lifted it quickly?

____

____

2. What variable did you change in Step 3?

____

3. Calculate the amount of work you did in Step 2 and the amount of work you did in Step 3.

____

____

4. Calculate the amount of power you used in Step 2 and Step 3.

____

____

5. In which step did you use more power? Explain.

____

____

Name ______________________ Date ____________ Class ____________

Inquiry Warm-Up

Is It a Machine?

Machines are devices that allow you to do work in an easier way. Machines can be very simple devices or very complicated. In this activity, you will examine a variety of objects and decide which are machines.

INQUIRY FOCUS Form an Operational Definition

Procedure

1. Examine the objects that your teacher gives you.
2. Sort the objects into those that are machines and those that are not machines.
3. Determine how each object that you classified as a machine functions. Explain each object to another student.

Materials

a variety of objects supplied by your teacher or found around the classroom

Think It Over

1. Why did you decide that certain objects were machines while others were not?

____

____

____

____

2. Choose three of the machines you identified. Name what type of simple machine it is and explain how it makes a job easier.

____

____

____

____

____

____

Name ______________________ Date______________ Class______________

Quick Lab

Going Up

Does a rope simply turn your force upside down? In this activity, you will lift an object using two different methods. You will compare the force required by each method and give a possible explanation for any differences.

INQUIRY FOCUS **Develop a Hypothesis**

Procedure

Materials

small cooking pot
50-cm string or twine
20-N spring scale
pencil

1. Read over the activity, and develop a hypothesis about the likely outcome of the activity.

   ____

   ____

2. Tie a piece of string (about 50 cm in length) to the handle of a small cooking pot. Make a small loop on the free end of the string.
3. Fix the string loop to a spring scale. Then, use the scale to slowly lift the pot 20 cm. Note the reading on the scale.
4. Loop the string over the pencil. Have another student hold the pencil. Pull down on the string with the spring scale to lift the pot 20 cm. Note the reading on the scale.

Think It Over

1. How did the scale readings compare to your hypothesis?

   ____

   ____

2. If the readings were different from Step 3 and Step 4, suggest a reason why.

   ____

   ____

3. What might be an advantage to using the second method for lifting an object?

   ____

   ____

   ____

Name ______________________ Date__________ Class__________

Quick Lab

15 min

Mechanical Advantage

Mechanical advantage describes how much a machine multiplies the force you exert. In this activity, you will determine which of two machines has the greater mechanical advantage.

INQUIRY FOCUS **Draw Conclusions**

Procedure

1. Place a 2-cm stack of newspapers next to the edge of a desk.
2. Insert a ruler under the stack so that about 15 cm of the ruler is resting on the desk.
3. Press on the end of the ruler to lift the papers. Note how hard or easy it is to press to lift the papers.
4. Replace the ruler with the meter stick and repeat the procedure.

Materials

meter stick
30-cm ruler
newspapers

Think It Over

1. What type of machine were you using in the activity?

____

____

2. Which machine had the greater mechanical advantage? How do you know?

____

____

____

3. Explain why the machine described in Question 2 had a greater mechanical advantage.

____

____

____

Name ____________________ Date __________ Class __________

Quick Lab — 10 min

Friction and Efficiency

Friction reduces the efficiency of a machine. Some of the input force is needed to overcome friction and is not available to do work. In this activity, you will rate scissors of differing tensions by their efficiency.

INQUIRY FOCUS **Classify**

Procedure

1. Use each pair of scissors given to you to cut paper. Note how easy or difficult it is to cut the paper.
2. After you use a pair of scissors, pass them on to another member of your group.
3. When everyone in your group has used each pair of scissors, work together to place the scissors in order from most efficient to least efficient.

Materials

several pairs of scissors with varying tensions

paper

Think It Over

1. What are some ways you could classify the scissors used by your group?

____

____

____

2. Why would you want to use scissors with a greater efficiency to cut paper?

____

____

____

3. What happens to the force required to cut paper if the friction in a pair of scissors is increased?

____

____

Name ______________________ Date ____________ Class ____________

Inquiry Warm-Up

Inclined Planes and Levers

Inclined planes and some levers are simple machines that reduce input force by spreading that force out over a greater distance. An example of an inclined plane is a handicap access ramp. An example of a lever is a hockey stick.

INQUIRY FOCUS Observe

Materials

ruler
pencil
0.5-kg weight
spring scale
loop of string, 6 cm in diameter
marker
masking tape

Procedure

1. Use the spring scale to lift the weight. Record the amount of force required. ____________
2. Use masking tape to label the ends of the ruler "A" and "B."
3. Place a pencil along the edge of a table. Place a ruler on the pencil at a right angle to it. Center the ruler on the pencil so side A is over the table and side B extends off the table. Place the 0.5-kg weight on side A about halfway between the pencil and the ruler end.
4. Hang the loop of string over the end of side B. Pull down on the string with the spring scale until the weight just lifts up off the table. Note the force required. Move the loop and repeat at several positions along that part of the ruler.
5. Now place end A on the pencil and hold it there. Put the string loop at end B. Place the weight close to end B. Use the spring scale to lift end B. Note the force required. Repeat several times, moving the weight closer to the pencil each time.

Think It Over

1. In Step 4, how did the amount of force needed to lift the weight compare to what you measured in Step 1? How did the force change at the different locations?

____

____

2. Assume you help a person in a wheelchair get from ground level to a platform raised two feet in the air. Think about the force required to lift the wheelchair straight up from the ground. Compare that to the force required to push the wheelchair up a long ramp. Which method do you think would require less force? In what way is an inclined plane similar to levers you explored in this activity?

____

____

Name ______________________ Date ____________ Class ____________

Lab Investigation

PRE LAB

Angling for Access

Reviewing Content

An inclined plane is a machine that helps us raise a load by spreading the work over a greater distance. The input force needed to pull or push the load along a ramp is much less than the output force, the weight of the object.

For example, to move a refrigerator up to a porch that is 2 m high, you might use a ramp that is 12 m long. You can calculate the ideal mechanical advantage (IMA) of an inclined plane by dividing the length of the ramp by its height:

$$\text{IMA} = \frac{12 \text{ m}}{2 \text{ m}} = 6$$

However, friction is always present, so the input force you need is determined by the actual mechanical advantage (AMA) of the ramp. You can calculate the AMA by dividing the weight of the load by the force actually needed to push it up the ramp. Suppose you push a 600-N load with a force of 200 N.

$$\text{AMA} = \frac{600 \text{ N}}{200 \text{ N}} = 3$$

In this lab, you will investigate the ideal properties of a ramp used for wheelchair access.

do the math!

Suppose your inclined plane is 60 cm long and it is raised 8 cm at one end. What is the ideal mechanical advantage of the inclined plane?

IMA = ________

Reviewing Inquiry Focus

When you interpret data, you analyze measurements and observations and draw a conclusion. If you made a hypothesis, you should decide whether or not your data support the hypothesis. If the data do not, it does not mean the experiment has failed. It simply means you should modify your hypothesis and then design a new experiment to test it. Preview the Lab Investigation. Then answer the questions.

1. What quantities will you measure in the lab? What are the units you will use when you collect data?

____

____

2. How do you expect the IMA to compare with the AMA?

____

____

Name _______________ Date _______________ Class _______________

DIRECTED Inquiry

Angling for Access

Problem

How does the steepness of an access ramp for wheelchairs affect its usefulness?

INQUIRY FOCUS
Interpret Data

Materials

- 4 books, about 2 cm thick
- metric ruler
- wooden block, with eyehook
- marker
- wooden board, approximately 10 cm × 50 cm
- spring scale, 0–10 N, or force sensor

Procedure

1. In this activity, you will make a model of a wheelchair ramp using a board and books. Read the following procedure. Predict the relationship between the slope of a ramp (inclined plane) and the force required to pull an object up the ramp. Write your hypothesis below.

   ____

   ____

   ____

2. The output force with an inclined plane is equal to the weight of the object. Lift the block with the spring scale to measure its weight. Record this value in the data table on the next page

3. Make a mark on the side of the board, about 3 cm from one end. Measure the length from the other end of the board to the mark and record it in the data table.

4. Place one end of the board on top of a book. The mark you made on the board should be even with the edge of the book. This will be the ending point for the load you will pull up the ramp. It is important that the ramp be set up in the same manner each time.

5. Measure the vertical distance (in centimeters) from the top of the table to where the underside of the board touches the book. Record this value in the data table under "Height of incline."

Name ____________________ Date__________ Class__________

6. Lay the block on its largest side with the end of the block aligned with the mark you drew on the board. Use the spring scale to pull the block straight up the incline at a slow, steady speed. Be sure to hold the spring scale parallel to the incline. Measure the force needed and record it in the data table.
7. Repeat Steps 4–6 using two, three, and four books to prop up one end of the board. Record the force needed for each trial.
8. For each trial, determine the ideal mechanical advantage and the actual mechanical advantage. Record the results of your calculations in the data table.

Data Table

Number of books	Output force (N)	Length of incline (cm)	Height of incline (cm)	Input force (N)	Ideal mechanical advantage	Actual mechanical advantage
1						
2						
3						
4						

Analyze and Conclude

1. **Interpret Data** For an individual trial, why did the ideal and actual mechanical advantages differ? Which one (IMA or AMA) would be more helpful in determining the ramp height that represents the best model for a wheelchair ramp? Why?

2. **Observe** What is the relationship between the height of the ramp and its ideal mechanical advantage? What is the relationship between the height of the ramp and its actual mechanical advantage?

3. **Draw Conclusions** Based on your answers to Questions 1 and 2, which ramp height represents the best model for a wheelchair ramp?

4. **Work With Design Constraints** How did the model help you determine the ramp's usefulness? What kind of limitations does your model have?

5. **Infer** In this activity, you were able to vary the height of the ramp. What other factor could you manipulate to change the mechanical advantage of the ramp?

Name ______________________ Date ____________ Class ____________

DIRECTED Inquiry — Lab Investigation

POST LAB

Angling for Access

1 **Design an Experiment** What changes could you make to the procedure to improve the accuracy of the results? How could you make the lab more closely resemble the way an actual wheelchair ramp works?

2 **Interpret Data** Suggest a design for a wheelchair access ramp leading to an entrance where there is not enough distance to install a long, straight ramp.

3 **Summarize** Describe what you learned about inclined planes (ramps) and their mechanical advantage, both ideal and actual, in this lab investigation. List any questions you still have.

What I learned

What I still want to know

Communicate

Analyze Experimental Results As a class, make a poster that includes the actual mechanical advantage data from each team. Then, compare the data. Choose another group's data and share with the class how the data compares to your own group's data. Discuss whether you can use the other group's data to reach the same conclusion that your group reached with its own data. Give reasons why or why not.

Name ______________________ Date ______________ Class ______________

OPEN Inquiry

Angling for Access

Problem

How does the steepness of an access ramp for wheelchairs affect its usefulness?

INQUIRY FOCUS
Interpret Data

Materials

- books, about 2 cm thick
- metric ruler
- wooden cart on wheels, with eyehook
- marker
- wooden board, approximately 30 cm × 100 cm
- spring scale, 0–10 N, or force sensor
- weights of various sizes (1N–5N)

Design an Experiment

1. There is a community center nearby that needs a handicap access ramp to the front door. The front door is 2 m above the ground. The only space available for the ramp is in front of the building in an area 12 m wide by 12 m long. The Americans with Disabilities Act (ADA) guidelines indicate that a handicap ramp must have an actual mechanical advantage (AMA) of at least 12. The ramp must be at least 1 m wide.
2. Use the formula for ideal mechanical advantage (IMA) to calculate the required length of the handicap ramp.
3. When scientists are designing products, they often use scale models to do preliminary testing. A scale model is a representation of the actual object, but is either smaller or larger than the object. Scale models help the scientist determine how the product might perform, but saves the scientist the cost of building a prototype. You will use the information you have about the ramp and its requirements to build a scale model for testing.
4. Use the following questions to guide you as you build your model.

   a. What materials will you use to make the ramp?

   b. What materials will represent the wheelchair?

   c. How can you use information from the formula for ideal mechanical advantage to set up a ramp that will meet the ADA guidelines?

   d. How can you determine the actual mechanical advantage of the ramp?

   e. How will you record and organize the data?

Name ______________________ Date ____________ Class ____________

5. Write out a detailed procedure of the scale model you will build and how you will perform the testing. Make a data table to record data.

Procedure

____

____

____

____

____

Data Table

6. Make a prediction about how the actual mechanical advantage will compare to the ideal mechanical advantage.

____

____

7. Have your teacher approve your design. Carry out your procedure and record your results in your data table.

8. After testing, if the actual mechanical advantage of your ramp is not at least 12, adjust your model until you reach this goal. Record your trials and results in your data table.

9. Given the results of your trials, determine if the length of the ramp will be different than the length you calculated in Step 1. If so, what will the length need to be? *Hint: You will need to use the height and length of your successful scale model to determine what the real-life ramp dimensions will be.*

Analyze and Conclude

1. **Interpret Data** What is the relationship between the manipulated and responding variables in your experiment? For example, what is the relationship between height of the ramp and ideal mechanical advantage?

2. **Make Models** How did the model help you design your wheelchair ramp? Does your model exactly represent the conditions of a real wheelchair ramp? Describe the differences between your model and an actual ramp.

3. **Infer** Now that you have built and tested a scale model and determined the length and layout of your actual ramp, what could you do to further test your design?

4. **Draw Conclusions** If an AMA of 12 for wheelchair ramps meets the requirements by law and is adequate, would a ramp with an AMA of 24 be even better since it requires even less force to push the wheelchair?

5. **Calculate** Suppose the wheelchair-access ramp to the door is also used to slide heavy cartons up to the door. Would the actual mechanical advantage be the same or different than when the ramp is used for wheelchairs? Explain your answer.

Name ______________________ Date ____________ Class ____________

OPEN Inquiry • Lab Investigation

POST LAB

Angling for Access

1. **Analyze Sources of Error** What sources of error exist in this lab? How can you minimize them?

2. **Infer** Imagine you are able to build a full-size model of part of the wheelchair ramp you have designed. You obtain a wheelchair to test the ramp. You find that the actual mechanical advantage of the full-size model is lower than that of your scale model. Propose an explanation for this difference. What changes will you need to make to your ramp so that it meets the ADA guidelines?

3. **Summarize** Describe what you learned about inclined planes (ramps) and their mechanical advantage, both ideal and actual, in this lab investigation. List what questions you still have.

What I learned

What I still want to know

Communicate

Design a Solution Suppose you have a friend living in another area who has a wheelchair-bound mother. Your friend is interested in designing a better access ramp for the entry to their house. Write a letter (or e-mail) to your friend explaining in detail how to design the ramp.

Name ________________ Date________ Class________

Quick Lab

Modeling Levers

There are three types of levers—first class, second class, and third class. In this activity, you will model each type of lever, and then identify the location of the input force, output force, and fulcrum.

INQUIRY FOCUS Make Models

Procedure

1. You or your partner will place an index finger flat on a table and balance a spoon on it. The other student will place a bean in the bowl of the spoon and demonstrate how pressing on the spoon handle allows them to lift the bean.
2. Place the bowl of the spoon on the table, and balance a bean on the middle of the spoon's handle. Have your partner carefully lift the edge of the handle.
3. Make a model of a third-class lever using a spoon, a bean, and a finger (if needed).

Materials

plastic spoons
dried beans

Think It Over

1. Identify the input force, the output force, and the fulcrum in the lever model you made in Step 1. What class of lever did you model?

____

____

____

2. Identify the input force, the output force, and the fulcrum in Step 2. What class of lever did you model?

____

____

____

3. Where are the input force, output force, and fulcrum in your model of a third-class lever?

____

____

____

Name ______________________ Date ____________ Class ____________

Inquiry Warm-Up

Machines That Turn

Have you ever tried to open a door when the doorknob is missing? It isn't easy. A doorknob and the attached shaft are an example of a wheel and axle, which make the work of opening a door much easier.

INQUIRY FOCUS Observe

Procedure

1. Insert one end of a wooden dowel into a large one-hole rubber stopper. Insert the dowel far enough that the stopper grips it firmly.
2. Have someone in your group hold the stopper and try to prevent it from turning while you try to turn the dowel.
3. Now have someone in your group hold the dowel and try to prevent it from turning while you try to turn the stopper.

Materials

- large 1-hole rubber stopper
- dowel, 10 cm long

Think It Over

1. Which took more effort—turning the wheel or turning the axle?

____

____

2. In terms of force, what is the purpose of using a wheel to turn an axle?

____

____

____

3. Some bank vaults have a large wheel to operate the latch. Why would they need a wheel that is much larger than a doorknob?

____

____

____

Name ______________________ Date ____________ Class ____________

Quick Lab — 15 min

Building Pulleys

How do different types of pulleys make work easier? In this activity, you will assemble models of pulleys, determine the mechanical advantage of each, and measure the amount of force required to lift a weight.

INQUIRY FOCUS Make Models

Procedure

1. Use the materials you have been given to assemble a model of one type of pulley shown in the figures of three pulley types in your student edition.
2. Use the spring scale to determine the amount of force required to lift the 1-kg mass. Record your measurement.
3. Repeat Steps 1 and 2 for the other two types of pulleys.

Materials

1-kg mass
2 pulleys
rope
spring scale

Think It Over

1. For each pulley, how much force was required to lift the mass?

____

____

____

2. What is the ideal mechanical advantage of each pulley?

____

____

____

3. In which pulley setup did you change the direction of the force?

____

____

Name ______________________ Date ____________ Class ____________

Quick Lab — 10 min

Machines in the Kitchen

In this activity, you will examine several common household tools and judge whether they are used as simple machines or combinations of simple machines in one compound machine.

INQUIRY FOCUS Classify

Procedure

1. Examine each object and visualize how it is used. If you do not recognize an object, discuss it with your group and make an educated guess about its use. Ask your teacher to see if you are correct.
2. Based on each object's characteristics and known function, determine if each object can be classified as a simple machine or compound machine.
3. Discuss the work each machine does and suggest how the machine makes the work easier or more convenient.

Materials

a variety of simple household objects supplied by your teacher

Think It Over

1. List three examples of machines you classified as simple machines. Describe how each machine makes work easier or more convenient.

____

____

____

2. List two examples of compound machines that you found. Note what simple machines each contains, and describe how the machine makes work easier or more convenient.

____

____

____

3. Did you observe any objects that can be used as two or more types of machines? Briefly describe each object and the work it performs.

____

____

____

CHAPTER 4

TABLE OF CONTENTS

Energy

Teacher Notes 92

What Is Energy?

Inquiry Warm-Up — How High Does a Ball Bounce? 99

Lab Investigation — Can You Feel the Power?
Pre Lab 100
Directed Inquiry 101
Open Inquiry 105

Quick Lab — Mass, Velocity, and Kinetic Energy 109

Forms of Energy

Inquiry Warm-Up — What Makes a Flashlight Shine? 110

Quick Lab — Determining Mechanical Energy 111

Quick Lab — Sources of Energy 112

Energy Transformations and Conservation

Inquiry Warm-Up — What Would Make a Card Jump? 113

Quick Lab — Soaring Straws 114

Quick Lab — Law of Conservation of Energy 115

What Is Energy?

Answering the Big Question

The activities in this lesson will help students answer the Big Question by having them observe the use of energy to do work and interpret power as the rate of work.

Inquiry Warm-Up

How High Does a Ball Bounce?

Inquiry Focus

Observe—using senses to gather information about the energy of a falling ball and how some of that energy is reclaimed when the ball bounces back

Group Size Pairs or groups

Class Time 10 minutes

Safety

1. Students should wear safety goggles throughout this activity.
2. Instruct students not to throw the balls at anyone or anything.

Advance Preparation

Check your tennis balls to be sure that they bounce back well. Discard those that appear to be "dead."

Alternative Materials

Any ball that bounces back well will work.

Procedure Tips

1. Suggest that students perform several trials at each position and find the average height of the bounce.
2. Encourage students to use the same method of observation in every trial.
3. For a dramatic comparison, have students test a "super ball" along with the tennis ball. A "dead" ball that doesn't bounce at all could also be tested.

Answers

1. Sample Answer: The ball has the greatest kinetic energy just as it contacts the floor.
2. Look for answers that suggest that the ball has the least kinetic energy when it is not moving just at the top of its bounce.
3. Sample Answer: The ball bounces the highest when it is dropped from the greatest height.
4. Look for answers that infer that the energy comes from the energy it had when it struck the floor. Some students might be able to add that kinetic energy changes to heat and potential energy, causing it to bounce.

Lab Investigation

Can You Feel the Power?

 Unlocking the Key Concept

Both Versions This activity will help students understand the relationships among energy, work, and power. First, students equate energy transfer to work and then see that power is the rate of work. which is also the same as the rate of energy transfer.

Answers—Pre Lab

Both Versions:

1. Height in meters, weight in newtons, and time in seconds.
2. Student A exerts more power because student A is heavier. Even though they do the same exercise in the same time, the weight lifted is greater for student A.

Answers—Do the Math

Gravitational potential energy = weight (N) × height of board (m)
The height, 15 cm, must be converted to meters.
Gravitational potential energy = 400 N × 0.15 m = 60 N•m = 60 J

Inquiry Focus

Directed Inquiry:

Interpret Data—analyzing and drawing conclusions from observations and numerical data. In this lab, students will draw conclusions about the rate at which energy is expended (power) in a standard stepping exercise and about differences in power from conducting the exercise at different speeds and with different weights

Open Inquiry:

Design an Experiment—using basic physical activities and materials to produce and measure work

Calculate—using data on work and rate to determine power

Interpret Data—comparing the power required by different people and different activities

Group Size

Directed Inquiry Pairs or groups
Open Inquiry Groups

Class Time

Both Versions 40 minutes

Safety

Both Versions:

1. Be sure partners hold the board steady and level throughout the investigations.
2. Partners should "spot" for steppers.
3. Review the Laboratory Safety Rules at the front of this book.
4. Instruct students not to jump on and off the board.

Advance Preparation (20 minutes)

Directed Inquiry:

1. Have the boards, stopwatches, and meter sticks ready.
2. Tell students to bring calculators and 2-cm thick books to class on lab day.
3. Provide bathroom scales so students can measure their weight.

Open Inquiry:

Gather the listed materials and identify locations or equipment needed for students to do some kind of repetitive movement, such stepping up onto a chair or bench whose height is easily measured.

Alternative Materials

Directed Inquiry:

The board required is popularly known as a "2 × 10" board, and should be 3 to 4 feet long. Boards that are 2 × 8 or 2 × 12 can also be used. Aerobic step apparatus can be used in place of the boards and books.

Procedure Tips

Directed Inquiry:

1. Students should recognize that the work done during the downward motion is done by gravity and cannot be counted as work done by the student.
2. A complete up-and-down cycle is counted as one repetition, not two.
3. Students' results should show that, for a given student, the work done for each repetition is the same because the step is the same height. However, slower repetitions mean lower power.
4. Tell students to convert pounds to newtons by multiplying pounds by 4.45 N/pound.

Open Inquiry:

1. Discuss the difference between work and power. Ask, **Does it take more work to walk up a flight of steps, or run up the same steps?** *(same amount of work)* Ask, **Which way requires more power?** *(running, because power is a measure of the rate at which work is done, and running is faster than walking)* Ask, **Is a 200-pound man leaping three feet into the air doing more work than a 150-hundred pound man leaping the same height?** *(Yes; there's more weight to be moved, so more work is being done.)* Explain that students will be designing an experiment to measure work and calculate power.
2. Go over the formulas that students will need to use to calculate work and power. If students have difficulty converting their own weight into newtons, provide a demonstration of this conversion:
   $$\text{(weight) lbs} \times \frac{1\text{ kg}}{2.2\text{ lb}} \times \frac{10\text{ m}}{\text{s}^2} =$$
   weight in newtons
3. Review the groups' procedures and data tables. For each student and each trial, they should plan to record the amount of time, the number of repetitions, and the amount of work per repetition (student's weight × height of step in meters). Work can be recorded for each trial if the height changes for some reason, but otherwise it should be calculated once and that same value should be applied to the power calculations. Students should plan to multiply work per repetition by the number of repetitions and then divide that by the time period over which the work was done. For example, 1200 Joules × 20 repetitions ÷ 30 seconds = 800 Joules per second.

Sample Data

weight × height:

$$160\text{ lbs} \times \frac{1\text{ kg}}{2.2\text{ lb}} \times \frac{10\text{ m}}{\text{s}^2} = 727.27\text{ newtons} = 730\text{N}$$

Work = 730 N × 0.46 m = 335.8 N•m = 336 N•m or 336 J

$$power = \frac{336\text{ J} \times 7\text{ repetitions}}{28\text{ s}} = 84\text{ J/s}$$

$$power = \frac{336\text{ J} \times 15\text{ repetitions}}{28\text{ s}} = 180\text{ J/s}$$

Answers—Analyze and Conclude

Directed Inquiry:

1. The amount of power was greater when the work was completed in a shorter time.
2. Students should calculate gravitational potential energy as weight in newtons multiplied by the height of the step in meters. Work and energy are the same in this case.
3. Students should realize that the amount of work done is the same in both trials, even though the times were different.
4. If the partners differed in weight, the amount of work done in 20 steps also differs. Power may or may not be different depending on the time used for the 20 steps. A lighter person might exert greater power if the rate of stepping is fast enough.
5. The amount of work is the same regardless of speed. However, more power is exerted by running up the steps because the work is done in a shorter time.

Open Inquiry:

1. Sample Answer: Weight varied from one person to the next. The heavier the person, the more work was required to step up onto the chair.
2. Sample Answer: The reduced rate meant less power was used. The more repetitions, the more power needed.
3. Look for answers that show the relationship between power and rate. The amount of work didn't change when rate was altered. Rate only affects power, not work. No matter how fast or slow the movement, the weight and height remained the same, and therefore so did the work.
4. Sample Answer: We recorded power in Joules per second. Because power equals work divided by time, the answer needs to be in the unit of work (Joules) per unit of time, seconds.
5. Look for answers that show students understand that no measurements were done to record the work required to lower themselves back down in a controlled manner. Some students might be able to offer an explanation and revision. For example; gravity does some of that work, but not all of it. We could revise the experiment so that we could climb a set of stairs as a result of each vertical step. The work to mount each step could be added up, or the entire height of the stairs could be treated as the total height, and the body weight in newtons could simply be multiplied by that height.

Answers—Post Lab

Directed Inquiry:

1. Sample Answer: An individual cannot instantly change their body weight. However, the person can add weights, increase the rate of stepping, or increase the height of the board while maintaining the same step rate.
2. One possibility is to have both persons step as fast as they can for a minute while another person counts the steps. The lighter person may be able to step fast enough to exert more power than the heavier person.
3. Students should realize that the power exerted depends on weight, height of step, and rate of step. Students may want to know how power output relates to food calories used in the exercise. They may also wonder what feature of human anatomy limits the practical height of the stepping surface.

Communicate—A parallel exercise could be done by having the person roll the wheelchair up a short ramp and back down repeating the exercise at a rapid rate. Various arrangements are possible using either one ramp, oscillating back and forth, or a series where the person rolls the wheelchair continuously.

Open Inquiry:

1. Sample Answer: The heavier twin does more work anytime he moves his body. Therefore, every step he takes when running or doing any other exercise involves moving more weight and therefore doing more work. All this work requires energy, which means he's burning through fat and calories faster than his lighter twin.
2. Sample Answer: We'd need to know the difference in height (in meters) between each floor, and the weight (in newtons) of the elevator car at the first, second, third, and fourth floors after passengers have gotten on. The amounts of work done to raise the elevator from one floor to the next could then be added up to get the total work done.

3. Students should realize that the power exerted depends on weight, height of step, and rate of step. Students may want to know how power output relates to food calories used in the exercise. They may also wonder what feature of human anatomy limits the practical height of the stepping surface.

Communicate—Student videos or diagrams should demonstrate that they understand the difference between work and power. The example should clearly point out how work would be calculated and how power would be calculated. All calculations should clearly show the units.

Quick Lab

Mass, Velocity, and Kinetic Energy

 Unlocking the Key Concept

This activity will help students understand that kinetic energy depends on both mass and speed.

Inquiry Focus

Control Variables—managing the conditions or factors in an experiment so that results from changing a single variable can be judged. Here, students must keep the kinetic energy of a rolling object equal in order to see the effect of changing the mass

Group Size Pairs or groups

Class Time 15 minutes

Materials

Any toy or other object that can be loaded and will roll freely is acceptable.

Safety

Tell students not to push the skateboard with so much force that it rolls across the room. A small push is more easily replicated.

Advance Preparation

Announce the lab a day ahead, determine which students might have skateboards or toy trucks at home, and ask those students to bring skateboards or toy trucks to class.

Procedure Tips

1. Imparting the same force to the skateboard results in the same kinetic energy. So, the board with more mass will move more slowly.
2. If students have trouble pushing the skateboard with the same amount of force each time, tie a meter or so of string to front of the skateboard. Attach a spring scale to the end of the string and have one students hold the board stationary while a second student pulls on the spring scale until the pointer reaches a specific force, such as 10 N. Then the student holding the board lets go. Repeat with the same force but a heavier load.

Answers

1. The kinetic energy is about the same, because approximately the same amount of work was done on the skateboard each time.
2. The velocity with one book was faster than the velocity with three books. The load with the greater mass was slower when the push was the same.
3. The push was held constant. The speed varied when the mass was changed. The kinetic energy was nearly constant.

Forms of Energy

 Answering the Big Question

The activities in this lesson will help students answer the Big Question by helping them understand that energy exists in forms other than mechanical energy, such as chemical energy, electrical energy, thermal energy, and electromagnetic energy.

Inquiry Warm-Up

What Makes a Flashlight Shine?

Inquiry Focus

Infer—drawing a conclusion about which forms of energy are involved and what transitions among these forms of energy take place based on observations of a flashlight

Group Size Individuals or pairs

Class Time 10 minutes

Materials

Flashlights that use standard incandescent bulbs work best. Those that use LEDs may be too cool. Provide an LED flashlight for comparison by students.

Safety
The bulb of an incandescent flashlight can become quite hot. Make sure students do not remove the protective faceplate of the flashlight.

Advance Preparation
A day ahead, find out which students will be able to bring working flashlights to class. Ask as many students as possible to bring in a working flashlight.

Procedure Tips
1. Consider using this activity to introduce the concept of chemical energy. Point out that the battery contains several substances that react chemically when the battery is connected to a circuit. The chemical energy released changes to electrical energy because it pushes an electric current through the circuit.
2. Students will observe light energy when the flashlight is turned on and feel thermal energy when they place their hand near the bulb.

Answers
1. Stored energy is released when the flashlight is turned on. Students should infer that batteries provide energy that is eventually changed to electromagnetic energy in the form of light.
2. Electrical energy comes from the batteries and travels to the bulb, where it is released as electromagnetic energy (light) and thermal energy.
3. Electrical energy changes to electromagnetic energy and thermal energy.

Quick Lab

Determining Mechanical Energy

Unlocking the Key Concept
This activity will allow students understand that the more mechanical energy an object has, the more work it can do.

Inquiry Focus
Interpret Data—making decisions about the relationship between mechanical energy and work

Group Size Pairs

Class Time 20 minutes

Advance Preparation (20 minutes)
Boxes should be large enough for students to drop the balls into the boxes without missing them. A box about the size of a shoebox should be sufficient. Pie plates can be substituted for the boxes.

Alternative Materials
Marbles can be substituted for the steel balls.

Sample Data
Ball mass was 27.2 grams.

Height	Diameter
25 cm	1.0 cm
50 cm	1.2 cm
75 cm	1.4 cm
100 cm	1.5 cm

Answers
1. Increasing the height increases the crater diameter.
2. Look for answers that indicate that the mechanical energy increases as the potential energy increases because the mechanical energy is equal to the sum of the potential energy and the kinetic energy.
3. Sample Answer: The more mechanical energy the ball has the more work it can do. The amount of work the ball does on the clay must be increasing because the diameter of the crater is increasing.

Quick Lab

Sources of Energy

Unlocking the Key Concept
This activity will allow students to recognize different forms of energy. They will also infer that energy can change forms.

Inquiry Focus
Infer—using the senses to observe how three devices work, and determining how energy changes forms in each of the devices

Group Size Pairs

Class Time 20 minutes

Advance Preparation (5 minutes)
Gather the required materials. Distribute them to each lab station.

Alternative Materials
Another spring toy or a "popper" toy could be substituted for a wind-up toy. Either a 1.5-volt or 6-volt dry cell could work.

Procedure Tips
Warn students not to turn the crank too fast in Step 2 or they could burn out the bulb.

Answers
1. The source of energy in the wind-up toy is the stored or elastic potential energy in the spring. The source of energy for the solar calculator is electromagnetic energy from a light source.
2. The wind-up toy produces kinetic energy. The solar calculator produces electrical energy.
3. Mechanical energy of the moving crank changes into electrical energy. Electrical energy changes into heat and light (or electromagnetic energy and thermal energy) in the light bulb.
4. A motor changes electrical energy into mechanical energy. A hand-held generator changes mechanical energy into electrical energy.

Energy Transformations and Conservation

Answering the Big Question
The activities in this lesson will help students answer the Big Question by demonstrating a transformation of energy from one form to another to show that energy is conserved and by helping them apply the law of conservation of energy.

Inquiry Warm-Up

What Would Make a Card Jump?

Inquiry Focus
Draw Conclusions—confirming or denying a hypothesis based on the interpretation of data involving potential energy changing to kinetic energy

Group Size Pairs

Class Time 10 minutes

Materials
Standard index cards work best although other stiff card stock may be used.

Safety
The card jumps unpredictably, so students should wear safety goggles.

Procedure Tips
1. The rubber band should be just large enough to stretch out when the card is flattened.
2. Students should wear safety goggles.

Answers
1. When the card is released, the rubber band snaps back and pulls the card with it.
2. When the card is flattened the rubber band is stretched, increasing its elastic potential energy. When the card is released, the rubber band contracts and its elastic potential energy changes to kinetic mechanical energy causing the card to move.
3. I could stretch the rubber band more.

Quick Lab

Soaring Straws

Unlocking the Key Concept
This activity will help students understand that energy can be changed from one form to another without being increased, lost, or destroyed. Here, they will increase the elastic potential energy of a rubber band and use that energy to increase the gravitational potential of a rocket-like object.

Inquiry Focus
Control Variables—managing the independent variable to obtain three different levels of elastic potential energy

Group Size Pairs or groups

Class Time 20 minutes

Materials
A few days ahead of this activity, ask students to bring toilet paper tubes from home.

Safety

1. Students must wear safety goggles.
2. Warn students not to point or shoot their rockets at another person.
3. Review the Laboratory Safety Rules at the front of this book.

Alternative Materials

If toilet paper tubes seem too flimsy, try sections of tubes that come with plastic wrap, aluminum foil, or wax paper. Short pieces of PVC drain pipe about 5 cm in diameter could be used as well.

Procedure Tips

1. Students may need to use 2 meter sticks taped end-to-end on the wall to provide enough height.
2. The straw rocket should be put on the rubber band the same way each time. The ends of the straw must be parallel when the straw is pulled down.
3. Review with students how to calculate gravitational potential energy.
   Gravitational potential energy (in joules) = weight (in newtons) × height (in meters)
   To get weight, they must convert grams to newtons by multiplying grams by 0.0098 N/g. Height should be in meters.

Answers

1. Graphs should show a nearly linear increase in gravitational potential energy with increasing stretch (elastic potential energy).
2. The number of centimeters the rocket is pulled into the tube (the stretch) indicates the amount of elastic potential energy. Therefore, the graphs should show a linear increase of gravitational potential energy with increasing elastic potential energy.

Quick Lab

Law of Conservation of Energy

Unlocking the Key Concept

This activity will help students understand transformations between kinetic and potential energy. They will also apply the law of conservation of energy to a practical situation.

Inquiry Focus

Develop a Hypothesis—using the concept of energy to explain why the height of a ball's bounce is not an inherent, fixed characteristic of the ball

Group Size Pairs

Class Time 20 minutes

Safety

1. Students should wear their safety goggles throughout this activity.
2. Students should stand clear of the balls in Step 3.

Advance Preparation

Plan on running the lab outdoors or in the gym because the tennis ball will bounce very high in Step 3.

Alternative Materials

Any two highly elastic balls will work, as long as one has more mass and is considerably larger than the other.

Procedure Tips

Sample Hypothesis for Procedure Step 2: The tennis ball will rise to a higher height when it is dropped on top of the basketball because it gets some elastic potential energy from the basketball.

Answers

1. Students should infer that the kinetic energy of the tennis ball just after the bounce is less than just before the bounce in Step 1 because the ball rises to a lower height than from which it was dropped. In Step 3, the opposite is true.
2. Sample Answer: Students should state that no energy is created or destroyed in this activity so energy is conserved. In Step 1, some of the tennis ball's initial gravitational potential energy is transformed to thermal energy because of friction between the ball and the ground. In Step 3, some of the basketball's initial gravitational potential energy is transformed to elastic potential energy and is passed on to the tennis ball. That is why it bounces so high the second time.

Name ______________________ Date ____________ Class ____________

Inquiry Warm-Up

10 min

How High Does a Ball Bounce?

Energy is the ability to do work or cause change. The kinetic energy of a falling object increases as it falls because its speed increases.

INQUIRY FOCUS Observe

Procedure

1. Hold a meter stick vertically, with the zero end on the ground.
2. Drop a tennis ball from the 50-cm mark and record the height to which it bounces.

   ____

3. Drop the ball from the 100-cm mark. Record the height to which it bounces.
4. Predict how high the ball will bounce if dropped from the 75-cm mark. Test your prediction.

   Prediction: ____________ Actual height: ____________

Materials

meter stick
tennis ball

Think It Over

1. At what point do you think the dropped ball has the most kinetic energy?

   ____

   ____

2. Where does the ball have the least kinetic energy after it bounces?

   ____

   ____

3. How does the height from which you drop the ball relate to the height to which the ball bounces?

   ____

   ____

4. Infer where the ball gets energy to bounce back up after striking the floor.

   ____

   ____

PRE LAB

Can You Feel the Power?

Reviewing Content

Power is the rate at which energy is transferred. Because energy is the ability to do work, power is also the rate at which work is done. One reason that we use machines is that many of them can do work at a faster rate than the human body alone. In other words, machines have greater power. Both work and energy are measured in joules, J. So power, the rate of work, is measured in joules per second, J/s. When you lift an object, you do work on it. The work you do is equal to the weight of the object in newtons multiplied by the vertical distance in meters you move it, work = weight × distance. When you calculate work this way, the result is in newton•meters, which is the same as joules.

do the math!

You gain gravitational potential energy every time you step up to a higher level. Gaining energy requires work.
gravitational potential energy = weight (N) × height (m)
Assume your weight is 400 N. If the height of a board is 15 cm, how much gravitational potential energy do you gain by stepping up once?

Reviewing Inquiry Focus

You make observations in every experiment. Sometimes you also make measurements. Both measurements and observations are data. You can interpret this data to learn about the questions that you tested in the experiment. In this lab, you will interpret data to compare the power used by several bodies in a "stepping" exercise. When different people with different weights do the exercise at different speeds, how does the power output vary?

With these statements in mind, preview the Lab Investigation. Then answer the questions in the spaces provided.

1. What are the three measurements you need to make in order to calculate power? What are the units of those measurements?

____

____

2. Suppose students A and B do the stepping exercise in equal amounts of time and at the same rate of speed. If student A is heavier than student B, which student exerts more power? Explain.

____

____

Name Date Class

DIRECTED Inquiry

Can You Feel the Power?

Problem

INQUIRY FOCUS
Interpret Data

Can you change how much power you use while exercising?

Materials

calculator
meter stick
stopwatch or clock with a second hand
board, about 4 cm × 25 cm × 120 cm
18–20 books, each about 2 cm thick

Procedure

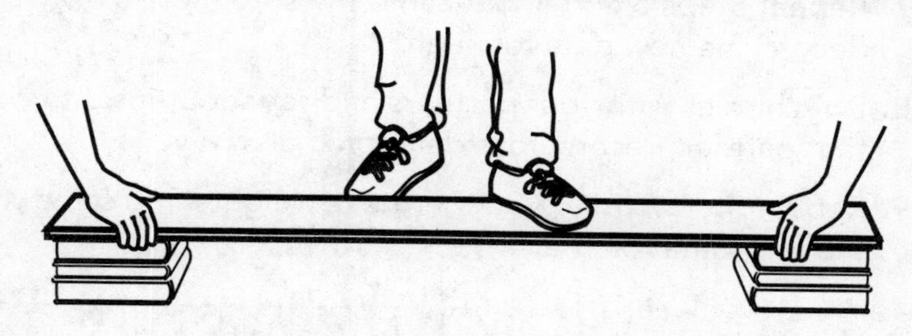

1. Construct a step by making two identical stacks of books. Each stack should be about 20 cm high. Place a board securely on top of the stacks of books so that the ends of the board are even with the outside edges of the books. **CAUTION:** ***Be sure to have your partners hold the board steady and level throughout the activity.***
2. Measure the vertical distance in centimeters from the floor to the top of the board. Convert to meters by dividing by 100 and record this height in the data table.
3. Step up onto the board with both feet and then step backwards off the board onto the floor. This up and down motion is one repetition. Make sure you are comfortable with the motion.
4. Calculate the work you do in stepping up onto the board once. Then calculate the work you would do by stepping up onto the board 20 times. Record both answers in your data table.

   your weight (N) × height of board (m) = gravitational potential energy = work done in stepping up onto board

Name ______________________ Date ____________ Class ____________

DIRECTED Inquiry • Lab Investigation

CAN YOU FEEL THE POWER? *continued*

5. Have one partner time how long it takes you to do 20 repetitions performed at a constant speed. Count out loud to help the timer keep track of the number of repetitions. Record the time in the Trial 1 row of your data table.

6. Calculate the work you did for 20 repetitions. Then calculate your power for the 20 repetitions. Record your data for Trial 1.

   power = energy transferred/time = work/time

7. Repeat Steps 5 and 6, but climb the step more slowly than you did the first time. Record the new data for Trial 2.

8. Switch roles with your partners and repeat Steps 3 through 6 using the weight of that partner. Record your data for Trial 3.

9. Repeat Step 7 using your partner's weight—the same weight used in Step 8. Record the new data for Trial 4.

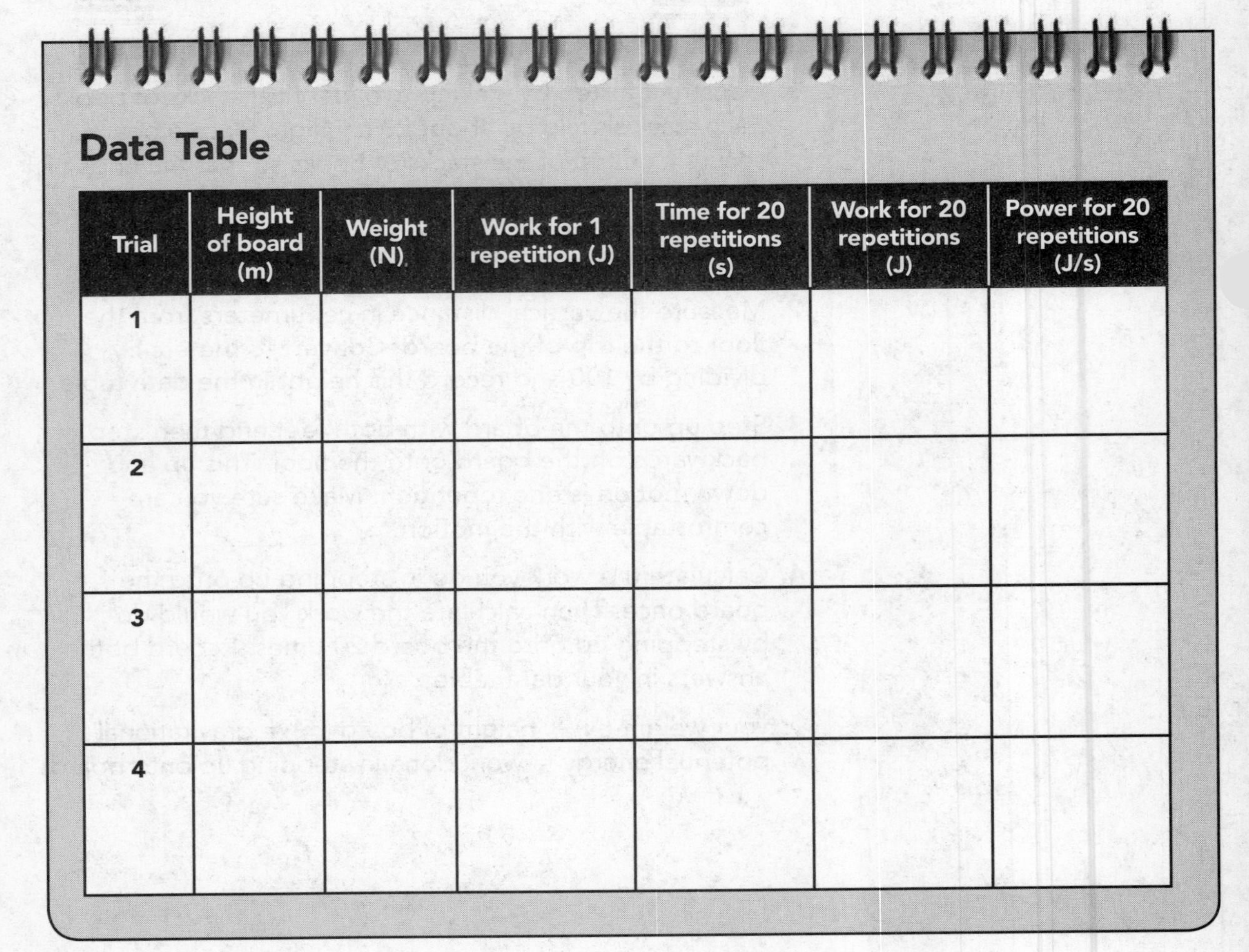

Data Table

Trial	Height of board (m)	Weight (N)	Work for 1 repetition (J)	Time for 20 repetitions (s)	Work for 20 repetitions (J)	Power for 20 repetitions (J/s)
1						
2						
3						
4						

Analyze and Conclude

1. **Interpret Data** Compare the amount of power you produced during your first and second trials.

2. **Calculate** What is the gravitational potential energy gained from stepping up onto the board? How does this amount of energy compare to the amount of work required to step up onto the board?

3. **Observe** Describe the amount of work you did during your first and second trials.

4. **Draw Conclusions** Did you and your partners do the same amount of work? Did you all produce the same amount of power? Explain your answers.

5. **Predict** Did you do more work walking up a flight of steps or running up the same steps? Did you exert more power? Explain.

Name ______________________ Date ____________ Class ____________

DIRECTED Inquiry • Lab Investigation

POST LAB

Can You Feel the Power?

1 **Draw Conclusions** Describe two ways that a single person doing the step exercise can change the power used? Explain your methods.

____

____

____

____

2 **Design an Experiment** Describe an experiment to determine which of two people of different weights could exert the greater power using the step apparatus.

____

____

____

____

____

3 **Summarize** Describe what you learned about the power exerted when a person does the step exercises. List any questions you still have.

What I learned

____

____

What I still want to know

____

____

Communicate

Build a Prototype Suppose you are asked to teach an exercise class for a group of people in wheelchairs. Think about how a person in a manual wheelchair might do exercises that are similar to the step exercises. Design a physical setup that would make such exercises possible. Draw a diagram of your setup and demonstrate it to the class. Develop a specific exercise routine, and explain the details during your class demonstration.

Name ______________________ Date ____________ Class ____________

OPEN Inquiry

40 min 

Can You Feel the Power?

Problem

INQUIRY FOCUS
Design an Experiment, Calculate, Interpret Data

Can you change how much power you use while exercising?

Materials

calculator
meter stick
stopwatch or clock
chair or bench

Design an Experiment

1. Imagine that you are arguing with a friend about the amount of physical strength it takes to leap up onto a table. The friend thinks that someone who is light in weight does more work than a larger person who can leap just as high. Their reasoning is, the smaller person probably has less muscle mass, and therefore a leap of equal height means more work is being done. You, on the other hand, have just learned the physical definition of work. So you know that the lighter person is actually doing less work than the heavier person. To prove your point, design a simple experiment to demonstrate how much work is done during a given physical movement and calculate how much power is required to repeat that movement over a given period of time.

2. You will need to use several formulas in your experiment:

   a. work (in Joules, or newton•meters) = weight (force in newtons) × height (in meters)

   b. (weight) lbs $\times \frac{1 \text{ kg}}{2.2 \text{ lb}} \times \frac{10 \text{ m}}{\text{s}^2}$ = weight in newtons

   c. power = work × time

3. With your partners, think about a physical movement or exercise you want to use in this activity. Your teacher will provide you with something you can step or hop onto. Your movement must involve moving vertically in a way that is easy to repeat and easy to measure. Each of you should take turns trying this movement and figuring out a pace that will allow you to repeat the movement over the course 20 or 30 seconds without risking injury or tiring yourself. Your paces can vary, but aim for a steady rate of movement for yourself.

4. Set up an experiment in which each of you, one at a time, repeats the movement at a regular pace over a given period of time. You will measure work and gather other data that will help you calculate power. Do at least one other trial where you perform the movement (work) at a slower pace. Describe your procedure and record data below. As you design your procedure, consider these questions:

- **a.** To measure how much work goes into moving a person's body vertically, what data do you need?
- **b.** What are the units for those data? Will you need to do any conversions?
- **c.** Power is a measure of the rate at which work is performed. To measure rate, what two things will you need to measure during each trial?
- **d.** How can you change the amount of power that is used without changing the time period or the work per movement?

5. Have your teacher review your procedure and data table. Once approved, carry out your procedure and record your results below.

Procedure

____

____

____

____

____

____

Data Table

Name ______________________ Date__________ Class__________

CAN YOU FEEL THE POWER? *continued*

OPEN Inquiry

Lab Investigation

Analyze and Conclude

1. **Calculate** When calculating work, what factor varied from one person to the next, and how did this factor affect the values you calculated?

2. **Interpret Data** How did power change when you reduced the rate of movement? Explain.

3. **Observe** Did work change when you reduced the rate of movement? Explain.

4. **Infer** What units did you use for power? Why?

5. **Design an Experiment** In terms of muscle work, energy, and physiology, this experiment failed to account for every bit of effort that your body had to make to complete each repetition. Why? How could you revise your experiment to correct this?

Name ______________________ Date__________ Class__________

OPEN Inquiry — Lab Investigation

POST LAB

Can You Feel the Power?

1. **Draw Conclusions** Imagine identical twins who are the same height and do the same physical activities, but one is heavier than the other. They go on a diet together. They eat the same foods, and do the same exercises each day, but the heavier one loses weight at a much faster rate than the other. Use your knowledge of work and power to explain this.

2. **Apply** How could you measure the amount of work done by an elevator as it moves from the first floor to the fifth floor and picks up one new passenger at each floor on the way up?

3. **Summarize** Describe what you learned about the power exerted when a person does the step exercises. List any questions you still have.

   What I learned

   What I still want to know

Communicate

Make a video or draw diagrams to explain the difference between work and power. Use a scenario to compare the difference, such as slowly lifting a barbell over your head versus lifting it over your head ten times in twenty seconds. Be sure to cover

- the influence of rate on power
- the units involved in calculating work and power
- practical applications of both measurements

Name ______________________ Date ____________ Class ____________

Quick Lab

Mass, Velocity, and Kinetic Energy

Any object in motion has kinetic energy. The amount of kinetic energy depends on the object's mass and how fast it is moving. In this activity, you will see how a constant kinetic energy affects speed when mass varies.

INQUIRY FOCUS Control Variables

Procedure

1. Place one book on the skateboard.
2. Push the skateboard, and observe the velocity at which the skateboard travels.
3. Place three books on the skateboard, push the skateboard with the same force as in Step 2. Observe the velocity of the skateboard.

Materials

skateboards or toy trucks
3 large books

Think It Over

1. What can you determine about the kinetic energy of the skateboard in the two trials?

____
____
____

2. How do the velocities in the two trials compare? Explain.

____
____
____

3. What factor was held constant in this experiment? What factors varied?

____
____
____

Name ______________________ Date __________ Class __________

Inquiry Warm-Up

What Makes a Flashlight Shine?

Energy is the ability to cause motion or change in matter. Sometimes that motion or change takes place among the atoms and molecules that make up matter. In this activity, you will observe changes in forms of energy.

INQUIRY FOCUS Infer

Procedure

Materials

flashlight
batteries

1. Remove the batteries from a flashlight and examine them. Think about what type of energy is stored in the batteries.
2. Replace the batteries and turn on the flashlight. What type of energy do you observe?

   ____

   ____

3. After a few minutes, place your hand near the bulb of the flashlight. What type of energy do you feel?

   ____

   ____

Think It Over

1. Describe how you think a flashlight works in terms of energy.

   ____

   ____

   ____

2. Where does the energy come from? Where does the energy go?

   ____

   ____

   ____

3. What change in energy takes place in the bulb of the flashlight?

   ____

   ____

Name ______________________ Date____________ Class____________

Quick Lab

Determining Mechanical Energy

An object has energy if it has the ability to do work on another object. In this activity, you will investigate the relationship between mechanical energy and work.

INQUIRY FOCUS Interpret Data

Procedure

1. Drop the ball into the box of clay from a height of 25 cm. Measure the height of the drop from the surface of the clay not from the floor or the tabletop. Record this height in the data table below.
2. Carefully remove the ball from the clay and measure and record the diameter of the crater that the ball formed. Smooth the crater out of the clay.
3. Repeat Steps 1 and 2, dropping the ball from heights of 50 cm, 75 cm, and 100 cm.

Materials

small steel ball
shoebox-bottom lined with soft modeling clay
meter stick
metric ruler

Height	Diameter

Think It Over

1. According to your data, how are crater diameter and the height of the ball related?

____

____

2. How does potential energy affect the ball's mechanical energy? Why?

____

____

3. How does mechanical energy relate to the work the ball can do? How do you know?

____

____

Name ______________________ Date ____________ Class ______________

Quick Lab — 20 min

Sources of Energy

Most devices must change one form of energy into another form of energy in order to work. In this activity, you will identify the forms of energy in a wind-up toy, a solar calculator, and a hand-held generator.

INQUIRY FOCUS Infer

Procedure

1. Examine the wind-up toy and the solar calculator. Determine how each one works.
2. Connect the wires of the hand-held generator to each side of the socket. Turn the crank on the generator. Observe what happens.
3. Connect the wires of the generator to the battery. Observe what happens.

Materials

wind-up toy
solar calculator
hand-held generator
dry cell
light bulb with socket
alligator clips

Think It Over

1. What is the source of energy in the wind-up toy and the solar calculator?

____

____

2. What form of energy did the wind-up toy and the solar calculator produce?

____

____

3. Describe how energy changed forms in Step 2 of the procedure.

____

____

4. In Step 3, the hand-held generator was run in reverse—like a motor. Explain why a motor is the reverse of a generator in terms of energy.

____

____

____

Name ______________________ Date__________ Class__________

Inquiry Warm-Up

What Would Make a Card Jump?

Energy is needed to cause an object to start moving, stop moving, speed up, slow down, or change direction. This energy can be transformed from other kinds of energy. In this activity, you will observe energy transformations.

INQUIRY FOCUS **Draw Conclusions**

Procedure

1. Fold an index card in half.
2. In the edge opposite the fold, cut two slits that are about 2 cm long and 2 cm apart. The slits should be cut through both halves of the card.
3. Keep the card folded and loop a rubber band through the slits. With the fold toward you, gently open the card like a tent and flatten it against your desk.
4. Predict what will happen to the card if you let go. Then test your prediction.

____

____

Materials

3 × 5 index card
scissors
rubber band

Think It Over

1. Describe what happened to the card.

____

____

2. Based on your observations, describe the forms of energy observed in this activity and the changes in energy that take place.

____

____

____

3. What can you do to increase the potential energy of a rubber band?

____

____

Name ______________________ Date ____________ Class ______________

Quick Lab

20 min 

Soaring Straws

The gravitational potential energy of an object depends on how far it can fall, and can be increased by raising the object to a greater height.

INQUIRY FOCUS Control Variables

Procedure

1. Make a launcher by cutting a rubber band and taping it across an open end of a toilet paper tube.
2. Tape the straws together at one end. Starting at the untaped end, make marks every 1 cm on one straw.
3. Measure the mass of the straws. ______________
4. Hold the launcher in one hand with your fingers over the rubber band ends. Place the rocket in the launcher, rest it on the rubber band, and pull down. Measure the stretch by the marks on the straw.
5. Align the top of the rocket with the bottom of a meter stick taped to a wall. Let go to launch the rocket. **CAUTION:** ***Aim the rocket in the air.***
6. Record the height to which the rocket rises. Repeat Steps 4 and 5 two more times.
7. Repeat Steps 4 through 6 using a different amount of stretch.
8. Calculate the average height and gravitational potential energy for each trial.

Materials

- scissors
- rubber band
- 2 plastic straws
- meter stick
- marker
- metric ruler
- balance
- masking tape
- empty toilet paper tube
- graph paper

Data Table

Amount of stretch (cm)	Height: Trial 1 (m)	Height: Trial 2 (m)	Height: Trial 3 (m)	Average height (m)	Gravitational potential energy (J)

Think It Over

1. Graph the gravitational potential energy versus amount of stretch.
2. In this experiment, what measurement is related to elastic potential energy? What relationship between the elastic potential energy of the rubber band and the gravitational potential energy of the rocket does your graph show?

____

____

Name ______________________ Date ____________ Class ____________

Quick Lab

Law of Conservation of Energy

Does a ball always rise to the same height after it is dropped from a height of 1 m? In this activity, you will find out. You will use the law of conservation of energy to explain your observations.

INQUIRY FOCUS **Develop a Hypothesis**

Procedure

1. Drop a tennis ball from a height of 1 m. Use the meter stick to measure how high it bounces. Record your result. ______________

2. Suppose you place the tennis ball on top of the basketball and drop both together from a height of 1 m. Predict whether the tennis ball will rise to a lower, the same, or a higher height than it did in Step 1. Develop a hypothesis to explain your prediction.

____

____

3. Test your hypothesis, and record your observations.

____

____

Materials

basketball
tennis ball
meter stick

Think It Over

1. In Steps 1 and 3, how does the kinetic energy of the tennis ball just after the bounce compare to just before the bounce? How do you know?

____

____

____

2. Explain why your answer to Step 3 agrees with the law of conservation of energy.

____

____

____

CHAPTER 5

TABLE OF CONTENTS

Thermal Energy and Heat

Teacher Notes 117

Temperature, Thermal Energy, and Heat

Inquiry Warm-Up — How Cold Is the Water? 124

Lab Investigation — Build Your Own Thermometer
Pre Lab 125
Directed Inquiry 126
Open Inquiry 130

Quick Lab — Temperature and Thermal Energy 134

The Transfer of Heat

Inquiry Warm-Up — What Does It Mean to Heat Up? 135

Quick Lab — Visualizing Convection Currents 136

Thermal Properties

Inquiry Warm-Up — Thermal Properties 137

Quick Lab — Frosty Balloons 138

Temperature, Thermal Energy, and Heat

Answering the Big Question

The activities in this lesson will help students answer the Big Question by observing materials of different temperatures, both subjectively and with a measuring instrument; making their own thermometer; and examining how the transfer of thermal energy makes a thermometer work.

Inquiry Warm-Up

How Cold Is the Water?

Inquiry Focus

Observe—using senses to gather information about the ability to judge temperature after exposing the hand to two different temperature extremes

Group Size Pairs or groups

Class Time 10 minutes

Advance Preparation (5 minutes)
Fill one or two clean buckets with tap water a day ahead of time so that the water will be at room temperature.

Alternative Materials

Any wide-based bowls or other containers are acceptable. Avoid small-based bowls that students may tip and slosh water.

Procedure Tips

Check the temperature of the warm tap water. Students should not use water with a temperature greater than 45°C.

Answers

1. Students are likely to describe the water in the bowls as cold, medium, and warm (or hot), respectively.
2. Sample Answer: The water in the third bowl (room temperature water) felt warm to the hand that was in the cold water and cold to the hand that was in warm water
3. Look for answers that show an understanding that the hand is not a good gauge of temperature because the feeling is relative.

Lab Investigation

Build Your Own Thermometer

Unlocking the Key Concept

Directed Inquiry This activity will help students understand that changes in thermal energy have an effect on matter.

Open Inquiry This activity will challenge students to use the expansion and contraction of liquids to design a thermometer.

Answers—Pre Lab

Both Versions:

1. Students should expect the water level to rise when the apparatus is placed in warm water and lower when it is placed in cold water.
2. Students could mark the straw with temperatures to match the actual temperatures. After measuring between the marks, they could calculate the levels where whole degree marks should be placed.

Inquiry Focus

Directed Inquiry:

Analyze Models and Systems—analyzing the extent to which the model thermometer successfully replicates the operation of a real-world thermometer

Open Inquiry:

Design a Solution—determining how to make and calibrate a homemade thermometer

Evaluate the Design—comparing homemade thermometers with manufactured thermometers

Group Size

Directed Inquiry Pairs or groups
Open Inquiry Pairs

Class Time

Both Versions 45 minutes

Safety

1. Caution students to be careful using thermometers, glass bottles, and hot water.
2. Remind students that food coloring stains clothing and skin.
3. Students should wear their safety goggles, apron, and gloves throughout the lab.

Advance Preparation (30 minutes)

Both Versions:

1. Gather the required materials.
2. Soften the clay to make it easier to work with.
3. To move the lab along and save time, set up several stations containing a hot water bath and ice water bath.
4. The water of unknown temperature should be hotter than the cold-water bath and cooler than the hot-water bath.

Alternative Materials

Directed Inquiry:

The following items can be substituted for the materials listed in the SE. One-hole rubber stopper, glass flask, plastic tubing, index cards, clear plastic bottles

Procedure Tips

Directed Inquiry:

1. Small diameter straws work better than large diameter straws. Very thick glass bottles should be avoided as they take too long to come to temperature.
2. Be certain students obtain an airtight seal with the clay.
3. It might be easier for some students to tilt the bottle and straw when adding water to the straw in Step 3.

Open Inquiry:

1. Make sure the straw is sticking up far enough above the rim of the bottle so the students can clearly see the change in the level of the liquid as a result of placing their thermometers in warm and cold water.
2. Have ice available to add to the cold water after placing the warm bottle in it.
3. Allow the thermometer to sit in the cold and hot water for several minutes to give it time to react.
4. If you have common hot water and ice baths, it may be helpful to keep an alcohol thermometer in each throughout the whole activity for students to reference.
5. Sample Answer to Procedure Step 3: Water level changes are more visible in the graduated cylinder.
6. Sample Answer to Procedure Step 4: a tall, thin container
7. Sample Answer to Procedure Step 6: Check students' designs. Refer to the Directed Inquiry version of this lab for one possible design. Be certain students obtain an airtight seal with the clay.

Answers—Analyze and Conclude

Directed Inquiry:

1. Sample Answer: The thermometer is a reasonable model of a real thermometer in that the liquid level rises and falls with changes in temperature. It is like a real thermometer in that it has a scale that can be used to measure temperatures. The actual scale intervals are arbitrary and different than in a real thermometer. Water expands when it is heated, like alcohol, but not to the same extent.
2. Look for answers that show an understanding of the relationship between matter and kinetic energy. When the thermometer is placed in hot water, thermal energy is transferred to the particles in the thermometer and these particles speed up (increase in kinetic energy) and spread out causing the liquid to expand. The reverse occurs when the thermometer is placed in ice water.
3. The thermometer measures temperatures between about 0°C (ice water) and 50°C (assuming this is the approximate temperature of the hot-water bath used.)
4. Sample Answer: Use a different liquid, one that expands more when heated to better imitate alcohol; use a narrower tube to get a longer scale; or use a finer scale to get more exact temperature measurements.

Open Inquiry:

1. Sample Answer: Using the temperatures of the hot-water and ice baths, I was able to determine a rough scale for my thermometer in terms of distance the water traveled up the column per °C. I could then determine the temperature of the unknown by comparing the water level of the thermometer to the two marks I made in Steps 8 and 9.
2. Sample Answer: The reading on my thermometer was eight degrees higher than the actual temperature according to the alcohol thermometer. A more accurate thermometer might have a taller, narrower, column of liquid, so the level would change more noticeably with temperature changes.

3. Sample Answer: Our thermometer is like a manufactured alcohol thermometer in that it has a scale that can be used to measure temperatures. The actual scale intervals are different than those of an alcohol thermometer, however, because the diameter of the thermometer column is different, and alcohol expands and contracts at a different rate than water does.
4. Look for answers that state that, when the thermometer is placed in hot water, thermal energy is transferred to the particles of water in the thermometer. An increase in the kinetic energy of the water occurs, which causes the water molecules to move faster and take up more space. The opposite occurs when the thermometer is placed in ice water.

Answers—Post Lab

Directed Inquiry:

1. Look for answers that show an understanding of heat as the transfer of thermal energy. They should describe the movement of thermal energy from warm water to the liquid in the thermometer.
2. Look for answers that show understanding of the relationship among temperature, mass, and thermal energy. To improve the experiment, equal volumes (masses) of water should be used in each container.
3. Sample Answer: An increase in kinetic energy is related to an increase in temperature, and an increase in kinetic energy of particles of matter causes matter to expand. This is what makes a thermometer work. Students might still want to know if other liquids can be used or are used in thermometers as well as what different scales are used and why.

Communicate—If students do not already know, point out that ordinary lab thermometers are alcohol thermometers. Brochures should relate common temperature reference points such as freezing and boiling points of water, common room temperature, body temperature (37°C), and summer and winter temperatures on both scales. Brochures should also show the direction of transfer of thermal energy to and from the thermometer.

Open Inquiry:

1. Sample Answer: The limits are 0°C and 100°C, because these are the respective freezing and boiling points of water. An alcohol thermometer does not have the same limits because alcohol has different freezing and boiling points.
2. Sample Answer: The hot air, liquid, and food between the lid and pan lost kinetic energy and contracted, causing suction. An easy way to fix this problem would be to heat up the frying pan again.
3. Sample Answer: An increase in kinetic energy is related to an increase in temperature, and an increase in kinetic energy of particles of matter causes matter to expand. This is what makes a thermometer work. Students might still want to know if other liquids can be used or are used in thermometers, as well as what different scales are used and why.

Communicate—Look for answers that indicate that students have developed an understanding of expanding and contracting liquids according to temperature, and how that property can be used to measure temperature. Sample Answer: The better thermometer will be the one with the finer gradations, and more accurate readings. Students should organize their conclusions into a format suitable for a presentation.

Quick Lab

Temperature and Thermal Energy

Unlocking the Key Concept

This activity will help students understand how temperature is related to the rate that thermal energy is transferred.

Inquiry Focus

Interpret Data—analyzing and drawing conclusions about the relationship between thermal energy and temperature based on the observed rate of temperature change of two different-temperature liquids

Group Size Groups

Class Time 20 minutes

Safety

1. Students should wear their safety goggles throughout the activity.
2. Remind students to be careful when handling glass test tubes and thermometers.
3. Also remind them to handle the hot water with care.

Advance Preparation

1. Punch holes in the lids for the test tube and the thermometer. Make them as far apart as possible.
2. The hot water should be about 40°C and the cold water about 5°C.
3. Foam cups with matching lids can be obtained in grocery, party-supply, restaurant supply, and office supply stores.
4. Practice the set-up to make sure that the size of the test tube and the hole in the lid allow the two thermometers be far enough apart.

Alternative Materials

Thin cardboard placed over the top of the cup can be used in place of the lids.

Procedure Tips

1. Tell students to be sure that the thermometer in the cup is not touching the test tube.
2. Have paper towels available to clean up spilled water.
3. Be sure the cup will stand up with the thermometers and test tube inserted. If it does not, clamp the test tube to a ring stand using a test-tube clamp. This will steady the whole setup.

Sample Data

See the sample data table below.

Answers

1. The thermal energy of the cold water increased with time. The thermal energy of the hot water decreased with time.
2. Look for answers that show understanding of the relationship between number of particles and the amount of thermal energy. The temperatures did not change at the same rate. The hot water temperature decreased faster than the cold water temperature increased. The rates are different because there was more cold water in the cup than hot water in the test tube.

The Transfer of Heat

Answering the Big Question

The activities in this lesson will help students answer the Big Question by showing them different rates at which heat is transferred from one place to another and by allowing them to demonstrate and observe convection.

Inquiry Warm-Up

What Does It Mean to Heat Up?

Inquiry Focus

Predict—observing the rate at which various materials conduct heat and then using that information to make an educated guess about the rate at which a different object will melt

Group Size Pairs or groups

Class Time 15 minutes

Advance Preparation (5 minutes)
Place small bits of butter on wax paper and freeze them at least a day before the activity.

Alternative Materials

A set of small rods made from different materials would be ideal. Solid margarine or shortening can replace the butter.

	Temperature (°C)									
	1 min	2 min	3 min	4 min	5 min	6 min	7 min	8 min	9 min	10 min
Cold water	19°	19°	19°	19°	19.5°	19.5°	19.5°	19.5°	19°	19°
Hot water	25°	21°	20°	19.5°	19.5°	19.5°	19°	19°	18.5°	18.5°

Procedure Tips

1. Try to obtain utensils that are all about the same length.
2. Remind students not to touch the hot water or taste the butter.
3. Tell students that they should wash the utensils in soapy water when finished.
4. After the lab, point out to students that thermal energy transferred from the hot water to the frozen butter by conduction, convection, and radiation. However, the heat transfer by convection and radiation were the same for each material. The only variable was heat transfer by conduction.

Answers

1. The butter melted on most of the utensils. If plastic or wood is used, the butter may not melt as a result of conduction, but rather because of warm air rising from the hot water.
2. Sample Answer: The time was different for different utensils. The butter melted faster on metal utensils compared to the wooden or plastic ones.
3. Look for answers that include statements about the heat moving along the utensils from the hot water toward the butter, but at a different rate for each material.
4. Sample Answer: The amount that each ice cube melts will change, but the relative rates for each utensil will stay the same. The utensil on which the most butter melted will be the utensil on which the most ice melts.

Quick Lab

Visualizing Convection Currents

Unlocking the Key Concept

This activity will help students understand the form of heat transfer known as convection by having them observe the interaction of two fluids of different densities.

Inquiry Focus

Predict—making an educated guess about how fluids at different temperatures can form a convection current based on observations of the interaction of hot and cold water

Group Size Pairs or groups

Class Time 20 minutes

Safety

1. Remind students that glassware is breakable and that the hot water could cause a burn.
2. Caution students that food coloring stains clothes and skin.

Advance Preparation (20 minutes)

1. To save time, prepare hot water with red food coloring and cold water with blue food coloring. Do not make the solutions too pale or too dark as the layers will be difficult to distinguish.
2. The hot water should be about 45°C and the cold water about 5°C.

Alternative Materials

Other colors of food colorings may be used. Darker colors are preferable.

Procedure Tips

1. Demonstrate how to place one layer of water on top of the other by gently squeezing a full dropper against the side of the test tube.
2. Tell students that a slight tilt of the test tube may aid the layering process.
3. Sample Prediction for Procedure Step 3: The cold and hot water will mix to make warm, purple water.
4. Sample Answer to Procedure Step 5: Nothing happened in the test tube with the cold water on the bottom. In the test tube with the hot water on the bottom, the cold water sank below the hot water.

Answers

1. Sample Answer: Cold water is more dense than hot water. When the hot water is on top of the cold water the more dense liquid is already at the bottom of the tube. When the cold water is on top of the hot water the more dense liquid sinks below the less dense one.
2. Look for answers that show an understanding of the relationship between density and convection currents. The form of heat transfer is convection because the red-colored hot water rises above the more dense cold water. This process creates a convection current.

Thermal Properties

Answering the Big Question

The activities in this lesson will help students answer the Big Question by comparing the rate of transfer of thermal energy using an insulator and a conductor and by observing how materials respond to increases and decreases in thermal energy.

Inquiry Warm-Up

Thermal Properties

Inquiry Focus

Analyze Experimental Results—interpreting and drawing conclusions from temperature data, correlating it to the rate of transfer of thermal energy from hot water through materials with different insulating and conducting properties

Group Size Groups

Class Time 20 minutes

Safety

1. Remind students that test tubes and thermometers break easily. Care should be taken to handle all of the glassware gently.
2. The hot water won't scald someone but care should be taken to avoid splashing and spilling.

Advance Preparation

Obtain thin test tubes that will fit in the rack when the materials are wrapped around them.

Alternative Materials

Other materials, such as plastic wrap or aluminum foil, could be placed around the test tubes. The fingers of old gloves can be used for one type of fabric (acrylic, wool, cotton). If a test tube rack is not available, or the wrapped test tubes will not fit into it, use plastic cups; the cups will weigh down so they will not tip over when the test tube and thermometer are inserted. Test tubes to consider for this lab: 13 mm × 100 mm.

Procedure Tips

1. Try to obtain a variety of fabric swatches. Then students can compare the insulating properties of various types of fabrics and thicknesses. Swatches could be cut from the better parts of worn-out clothing.
2. Tell students that laboratory thermometers do not work like fever thermometers. They must not be "shaken down" and they must be read while they are immersed in the water.
3. Point out to students that the third test tube is the control. The rubber band is wrapped around the test tube so that the thermal properties of the fabric and paper clips can be measured. If the third test tube is bare, another variable (the rubber band) is introduced into the experiment.

Sample Data

	Tube 1	Tube 2	Tube 3
Material around tube	cloth	paper clips	none
Initial temperature	52	52	52
1 min	50	47	48
2 min	48	45	47
3 min	47	43	45
4 min	46	42	43

Answers

1. Students should observe that the tube wrapped with paper clips loses thermal energy the fastest. The temperature decreased most rapidly. Generally, the tube wrapped in the swatch should lose thermal energy the slowest. The temperature decreased the least rapidly.
2. Sample Answer: Paper clips are metal, and metals are good conductors of thermal energy. The paper clips conducted thermal energy rapidly away from the glass walls of the test tube, lowering the temperature of the water inside. Cloth has insulating properties. The tube wrapped in cloth did not lose thermal energy as rapidly as the other two test tubes.

Quick Lab

Frosty Balloons

Unlocking the Key Concept

This activity will help students understand that materials respond to increases in thermal energy by expanding and to decreases in thermal energy by contracting. Students will relate these effects to molecular motion.

Inquiry Focus

Infer—suggesting a possible explanation for the change in size of an object when it is cooled or heated

Group Size Pairs or groups

Class Time 20 minutes

Safety

Balloons are not to be played with. Instruct students not to overinflate the balloons and not to inhale while balloons are in their mouths.

Advance Preparation (30 minutes)

1. Place one large bag of ice in a large freezer chest or cooler at least 30 minutes before class. Keep the lid tightly closed.
2. Distribute materials to lab stations.
3. Pre-stretch the balloons to make inflation easier.

Alternative Materials

If you lack cloth measuring tapes, have students wrap a string around the balloon, marking where the end overlaps with a thumbnail. Students can measure the string using a ruler or meter stick.

Procedure Tips

1. Use small party balloons that inflate into a small spherical shape.
2. Balloons can cool for more than 15 minutes. Students can set up the lab at the beginning of the period and then measure the balloons again just before the end of the period.
3. Tell students to try to handle the cool balloon as little as possible.

Answers

1. Sample Answer: The balloons were roughly similar in size at first. Then, the cooled balloon decreased in size while the second balloon stayed about the same.
2. Look for answers that show an understanding of the relationship between thermal energy and particle motion. Student explanations should reflect the idea that thermal energy decreases as temperature decreases. This allows particles to move closer together. Thus, the balloon shrinks when cooled.

Name ______________________ Date ____________ Class ____________

Inquiry Warm-Up

How Cold Is the Water?

The temperature of an object depends on the average kinetic energy of the particles that make up the object. Temperature can be measured with a thermometer. But, how well can you judge temperature using your hand?

INQUIRY FOCUS **Observe**

Procedure

1. Fill a plastic bowl with cold water, another with warm water, and a third with water at room temperature. Label each bowl and line them up.
2. Dip your fingers briefly in each bowl to test how the water feels.
3. Place your right hand in the cold water and your left hand in the warm water.
4. After one minute, place both your hands in the third bowl at the same time.

Materials

- 3 large bowls
- warm tap water
- cold tap water
- room temperature water
- markers
- paper

Think It Over

1. How did the water in the third bowl feel when you touched it?

____

____

2. Did the water feel the same on both hands in Step 4? If not, explain why.

____

____

____

3. Do you think you could use your hands to judge temperature? Why or why not?

____

____

____

Name ______________________ Date__________ Class__________

Lab Investigation

PRE LAB

Build Your Own Thermometer

Reviewing Content

The particles of matter are in constant motion. The energy of motion is called kinetic energy, so the particles of matter have kinetic energy. As matter becomes warmer, its particles move faster. As a result, their kinetic energy increases. Temperature is related to kinetic energy. As temperature increases, kinetic energy also increases.

One way to measure the temperature of matter is to place a thermometer in contact with it. Some of the matter's kinetic energy is transferred to the thermometer if the matter is warmer than the thermometer. The increased kinetic energy causes the particles of the liquid in the thermometer to move farther away from each other. As a result, the liquid in the thermometer expands and rises up the tube. If the matter is colder than the thermometer, the thermometer loses energy to the matter. This makes the particles of the liquid in the thermometer move closer to each other, causing the liquid to contract and drop in the tube.

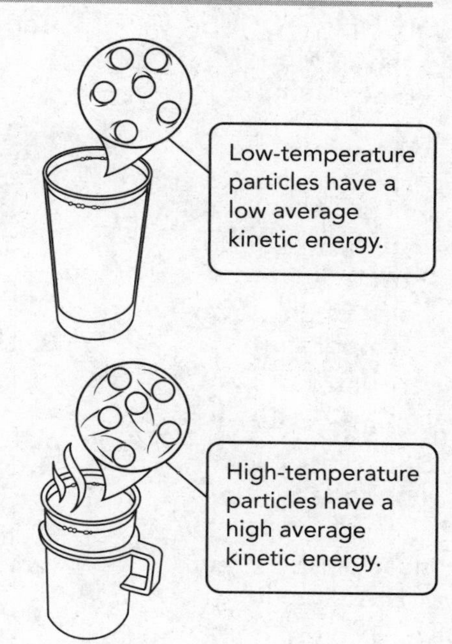

Reviewing Inquiry Focus

When you analyze a model, you determine how well the model can be used to predict what happens in the real world. In this lab, you will put together a combination of materials that simulates how a real thermometer works. Then you will test it to see if it behaves like a real thermometer when it is placed in contact with warm water and then cold water. With these statements in mind, preview the Lab Investigation. Then answer the questions.

1. How do you expect the water level to change when the apparatus is placed in warm water? In cool water?

____

____

2. If you had a real thermometer that was accurate, how could you modify your experimental thermometer to read actual temperatures?

____

____

Name ______________________ Date______________ Class______________

DIRECTED Inquiry

Build Your Own Thermometer

Problem

INQUIRY FOCUS
Analyze Models and Systems

Can you build a thermometer out of simple materials?

Materials

bowl of hot water
bowl of ice water
water of unknown temperature
tap water
600-mL beaker
clear glass juice or soda bottle, 20–25 cm tall
clear plastic straw, 18–20 cm long
food coloring
plastic dropper
cooking oil
modeling clay
metric ruler
fine-point marker

Procedure

1. Mix four drops of food coloring into a beaker of tap water.
2. Fill the glass bottle with the colored water.
3. Use a dropper to adjust the level of colored water in the bottle so that it is completely full to the top of the bottle.
4. Place a straw in the bottle. Use modeling clay to position the straw so it extends at least 10 cm above the mouth of the bottle. Do not let the straw touch the bottom. The clay should completely seal off the bottle's mouth. Make sure there is as little air as possible in the bottle.
5. Using a dropper, add colored water into the straw to a level 5 cm above the bottle.
6. Place a drop of cooking oil in the straw to prevent evaporation of the water.
7. Place your thermometer into a bowl of hot water.
8. When the colored water reaches its highest level, use the fine-point marker to place a mark on the straw.
9. Place your thermometer in the bowl of ice water.

BUILD YOUR OWN THERMOMETER *continued*

10. Place a mark on the straw when the water reaches its lowest level.

11. Create a scale for your model thermometer. Divide the distance between the two marks into 5-mm intervals. Starting with the lowest point, label the intervals on the straw 0, 1, 2, 3, and so on. Describe your scale below.

____

____

____

12. Measure the temperature of two unknown samples with your thermometer.

13. Record both temperatures using the scale on the straw.

____

____

Analyze and Conclude

1. **Analyze Models and Systems** Do you think your model accurately represents an alcohol thermometer? How is it like a manufactured thermometer? How is it different?

2. **Infer** How can you use the concepts of matter and the kinetic energy of particles to explain the way your model works?

3. **Measure** Approximately what Celsius temperatures do you think your model measures? Explain your estimate.

4. **Redesign** Examine the structure and materials used in your model. Propose a change that would improve the model. Explain your choice.

Name ______________________ Date ____________ Class ____________

POST LAB

Build Your Own Thermometer

1. **Draw Conclusions** In terms of thermal energy and heat, describe what happened when you placed your model thermometer in warm water.

____

____

____

2. **Infer** Do you think your model thermometer would be practical for measuring the temperature of small amounts of material? Explain.

____

____

____

3. **Summarize** Describe what you learned about how thermometers work and how they relate to the kinetic energy of particles of matter. List any questions you still have.

What I learned ____

____

____

What I still want to know ____

____

____

Communicate

Create a brochure to show how an alcohol thermometer works. Explain how the Celsius and Fahrenheit scales compare. For example, does 0° have the same meaning on each scale? What is normal body temperature on each scale? Use a diagram with labels and captions to communicate your ideas.

OPEN Inquiry

Build Your Own Thermometer

Problem

Can you build a thermometer out of simple materials?

INQUIRY FOCUS
Design a Solution, Evaluate the Design

Materials

- bowl of hot water
- bowl of ice water
- water of unknown temperature
- tap water
- 600-mL beaker
- graduated cylinder
- clear glass juice or soda bottle, 20–25 cm tall
- clear plastic straw, 18–25 cm long
- food coloring
- plastic dropper
- cooking oil
- modeling clay
- metric ruler
- fine-point marker
- alcohol thermometer

Design an Experiment

1. You are a geologist who wants to determine which of two springs is warmer. They are both too acidic to touch. Design and make a thermometer that will allow you to tell which liquid is warmer.

Part 1: Finding the Right Container Type

2. The levels in liquid thermometers change because liquids typically expand when they are heated and contract when they cool. However, these changes may be too small to easily see. First, you must determine what shape of container will allow you to better observe small changes in volume. Fill your graduated cylinder and your 500-mL beaker each halfway with water.
3. Add small amounts of water to each container. Observe what happens.
4. Based on observations, will it be easier to see small changes in a tall, thin container, or in a wide container?

____

Part 2: Designing a Thermometer

5. ⚠ Work with your partner to design a thermometer. Keep in mind:

   a. Food coloring can make water more visible.

   b. Most thermometers consist of a narrow column and a bulb that feeds into the column. The bulb contains a large volume of water that expands into the column when heated.

   c. The liquid in your thermometer should have no air bubbles.

   d. A drop of cooking oil can be placed in your thermometer to prevent evaporation.

6. Draw your design in the space below.

7. Have your teacher check your thermometer design. Then, build your thermometer.
8. Place your homemade thermometer in the bowl of hot water. Use the fine-point marker to mark the level that the water in your thermometer reaches.
9. Place your homemade thermometer in the bowl of cold water. Mark the level that the water in your thermometer reaches.
10. Using the manufactured thermometer, determine the actual temperatures, in °C, of the bowls of hot and cold water. Record them below.

    Hot water: ______________ Cold water: ______________
11. Write these values next to the marks you made on your homemade thermometer in Steps 8 and 9.
12. Using the information from Step 10, determine a rough scale for your homemade thermometer. Make and label appropriately spaced marks along the side of your homemade thermometer so you can measure any temperature between those of the hot water from Step 8 and the cold water from Step 9.
13. Using your homemade thermometer, work with your partner to determine the temperature, in °C, of the bowl of water of unknown temperature. Record your result. ______________
14. Check your result with the manufactured thermometer.

    Temperature according to manufactured thermometer: ______________

Name ______________________ Date ____________ Class ____________

OPEN Inquiry — Lab Investigation

BUILD YOUR OWN THERMOMETER *continued*

Analyze and Conclude

1. **Design a Solution** How did you use the two readings from the bowls of hot and cold water to determine the temperature of the unknown bowl of water?

2. **Evaluate the Design** Did your thermometer provide an accurate reading of the unknown water temperature? How could you design a more accurate thermometer?

3. **Observe** How is your thermometer like a manufactured alcohol thermometer? How is it different?

4. **Infer** Use the concepts of matter and the kinetic energy of particles to explain how your model works.

Name ____________________ Date __________ Class __________

OPEN Inquiry — Lab Investigation

POST LAB

Build Your Own Thermometer

1 **Evaluate the Design** What are the temperature limits of your thermometer in °C? Do alcohol thermometers have the same limits? Why or why not?

____

____

____

____

2 **Design a Solution** Imagine you are cooking with a frying pan. Once it gets hot, you cover it with a lid, and the lid makes a complete seal around the frying pan. Within 2 minutes, the lid becomes stuck to the the frying pan, with your food inside! In terms of matter and kinetic energy, how did the lid become stuck to the pan? How could you fix this problem? *Hint: The lid is like a suction cup.*

____

____

____

____

3 **Summarize** Describe what you learned about how thermometers work and how they relate to the kinetic energy of particles of matter. List any questions you still have.

What I learned

____

____

____

What I still want to know

____

____

____

Communicate

Evaluate the Design Join with another set of partners in your class. Compare and contrast your thermometer designs. Examine the data collected from both thermometers and decide which group built a better thermometer. What aspects made this thermometer better? Be prepared to share your results with the class.

Name ________________ Date ________ Class ________

Quick Lab

Temperature and Thermal Energy

Temperature is a measure of the average kinetic energy of the particles in an object. In this activity, you will observe what happens when thermal energy moves from one object to another and how temperatures is affected.

INQUIRY FOCUS **Interpret Data**

Procedure

1. Put on your safety goggles and apron. Fill a foam cup with cold water until it is about 5 cm deep. Place a prepared lid on the cup and put a thermometer through the small hole in the lid.
2. Pour hot water into a test tube until it is about 5 cm deep. Put a thermometer into the hot water.
3. Put the test tube through the large hole in the lid and have it rest on the bottom of the cup.
4. Read the temperature of the water in the cup and the water in the test tube every minute for 10 minutes. Record your data in the table below.

Materials

- test tube and test tube holder
- foam cup with prepared lid
- cold water and hot water
- 2 thermometers
- stopwatch or analog clock with a second hand

	Temperature (°C)									
	1 min	2 min	3 min	4 min	5 min	6 min	7 min	8 min	9 min	10 min
Cold water										
Hot water										

Think It Over

1. How did the thermal energy of the cold water change with time? The hot water?

____

____

2. Did both temperatures change at the same rate? Explain why or why not.

____

____

Name ______________________ Date______________ Class______________

Inquiry Warm-Up

What Does It Mean to Heat Up?

The time required for an object to heat up depends on the material from which that object is made. In this activity, you will investigate how different materials conduct heat.

INQUIRY FOCUS Predict

Procedure

1. Obtain several utensils made of different materials, such as silver, stainless steel, copper, ceramic, plastic, and wood.
2. Stand the utensils in a beaker so that they do not touch each other.
3. Press a small gob of frozen butter on the handle of each utensil. Make sure that when the utensils stand on end, the butter is at the same height on each one. Quickly wash your hands when you are finished.
4. Carefully pour hot water into the beaker until it is about 6 cm below the butter. Observe the butter on the utensils for several minutes.

Materials

- frozen butter
- glass beaker or jar
- hot water
- utensils made of different materials

Think It Over

1. Did the same thing happen on every utensil? Describe your observations.

____

____

2. Was the time required for this to happen the same for all the utensils? Explain.

____

____

3. How can you account for your observations?

____

____

4. How would your results change if you attached an ice cube to each utensil instead of frozen butter?

____

____

Name ______________________ Date ____________ Class ____________

Quick Lab

Visualizing Convection Currents

Convection currents are one way that heat is transferred from one place to another. In this activity, you will observe what happens when a hot liquid and a cold liquid interact.

INQUIRY FOCUS Predict

Materials

- 2 test tubes
- test tube holder
- red and blue food coloring
- cold water
- hot water
- 2 250-mL beakers
- large dropper
- plastic spoon

Procedure

1. Fill one beaker with 100 mL of cold water. Add three drops of blue food coloring and mix well. Fill one test tube about half-full with blue-colored cold water.
2. Fill the other beaker with 100 mL of hot water. Add three drops of red food coloring and mix well. Fill the second test tube half full with red-colored hot water.
3. Read Step 4 and predict what will happen to each test tube.

   ____

   ____

4. Use a dropper to add a 1-cm-thick layer of red-colored hot water to the test tube containing the blue-colored cold water. Then add a 1-cm-thick layer of blue-colored cold water to the test tube containing the red-colored hot water.
5. Observe both test tubes for a few minutes and record what happens.

   ____

   ____

Think It Over

1. How does the concept of density explain the different results with the two test tubes?

   ____

   ____

2. What form of heat transfer did you witness in Step 4?

   ____

   ____

Name ______________________ Date__________ Class__________

Inquiry Warm-Up — 20 min

Thermal Properties

Thermal properties of a material describe how it responds to heat. Some materials conduct thermal energy well. These materials are called conductors.

INQUIRY FOCUS Analyze Experimental Results

Procedure

1. Put on your safety goggles and apron. Wrap fabric around the first test tube and secure with two rubber bands. Secure 5 or 6 large paper clips to the second test tube with two rubber bands. Wrap two rubber bands around a third test tube, which will be the control.
2. Secure a thermometer in each test tube with a rubber band. Use small pieces of modeling clay to keep the thermometer bulb suspended in the tube but not touching the sides of the test tube. Place each setup in the test tube rack.
3. Remove the thermometers and clay from the test tubes. Use the funnel and beaker tongs to handle the beaker to fill each test tube about $\frac{3}{4}$ full with hot tap water. **CAUTION:** ***Be careful not to splash the hot water onto your skin.***
4. Reinsert the thermometers and secure them with the clay. Read the thermometers immediately and again every minute for 10 minutes. Record the temperatures in the data table. Add rows as needed.

Materials

- 3 test tubes
- 3 thermometers
- hot tap water
- beaker
- beaker tongs
- funnel
- test tube rack
- fabric swatch
- rubber bands
- large paper clips
- modeling clay

Data Table

	Tube 1	Tube 2	Tube 3
Material around tube	cloth	paper clips	none
Initial temperature			
1 min			
2 min			
3 min			

Think It Over

1. In which tube did water lose thermal energy the fastest? The slowest? Explain.

____

2. How can you explain the differences in the rate of transfer of thermal energy?

____

Name ______________________ Date ____________ Class ____________

Quick Lab

20 min

Frosty Balloons

Nearly all matter expands when its temperature increases and contracts when its temperature decreases. When temperature decreases, particle motion slows down, and particles move closer together.

INQUIRY FOCUS Infer

Procedure

1. Blow up two balloons so that they are the same size.
2. Use a measuring tape to measure the circumference of the balloons. Record these measurements on the lines below. Mark where you measure the balloons so that you can measure at the same place later.

____

____

3. Place one of the balloons in the freezer chest for 10 minutes.
4. Remove the balloon from the freezer and very quickly measure its circumference again. Try not to handle the balloon any more than is necessary.
5. Measure the second balloon again. Record the measurement on the line below.

____

Materials

2 small balloons
measuring tape
freezer chest with ice
marker

Think It Over

1. How did the circumference of the two balloons compare before and after one balloon was cooled?

____

____

2. Explain how changes in thermal energy caused the change in size.

____

____

____

CHAPTER 6

TABLE OF CONTENTS

Electricity

Teacher Notes 140

Electric Charge and Static Electricity

Inquiry Warm-Up	Can You Move a Can Without Touching It?	148
Quick Lab	Drawing Conclusions	149
Quick Lab	Sparks Are Flying	150

Electric Current

Inquiry Warm-Up	How Can Current Be Measured?	151
Quick Lab	Producing Electric Current	152
Quick Lab	Conductors and Insulators	153
Quick Lab	Modeling Potential Difference	154

Electric Circuits

Inquiry Warm-Up	Do the Lights Keep Shining?	155
Quick Lab	Ohm's Law	156
Lab Investigation	Build a Flashlight — *Pre Lab*	157
	Directed Inquiry	158
	Open Inquiry	162

Electric Power and Safety

Inquiry Warm-Up	How Can You Make a Bulb Burn More Brightly?	166
Quick Lab	Calculating Electric Power and Energy Use	167
Quick Lab	Electric Shock and Short Circuit Safety	168

Electric Charge and Static Electricity

Answering the Big Question

The activities in this lesson will help students answer the Big Question by having them explore how static electricity charges transfer and interact.

Inquiry Warm-Up

Can You Move a Can Without Touching It?

Inquiry Focus

Infer—using prior knowledge and observations to suggest a possible explanation for moving a can with a charged object

Group Size Pairs

Class Time 10 minutes

Procedure Tips

Make sure that students rub the balloon vigorously. Results are best when the air is dry.

Answers

1. Sample Answer: The can will follow the balloon in either direction.
2. There is a force attracting the can to the balloon.
3. Look for answers that suggest that the energy students used to rub the balloon was converted, or transformed, into a type of energy that could move the can.

Quick Lab

Drawing Conclusions

Unlocking the Key Concept

This activity will help students understand that uncharged, or neutral, objects are able to be attracted to a charged object.

Inquiry Focus

Draw Conclusions—using observations and prior knowledge to draw conclusions about a charged comb and its influence on uncharged pieces of paper

Group Size Pairs or groups

Class Time 10 minutes

Alternative Materials

Small hole-punch circles cut from regular paper may be substituted for tissue paper.

Procedure Tips

1. Avoid performing the activity on damp or rainy days.
2. Students may be puzzled how the uncharged paper is attracted. While the paper has a net neutral charge, it is made of equal numbers of positive and negative charges. When a charged object is brought near an uncharged object, only the electrons in the uncharged object will move close to the object if it is positively charged and farther away if it is negatively charged. Either way, the attracted charges are now closer to the charged object, and the uncharged object as a whole will be attracted.

Answers

1. Sample Answer: The comb was uncharged in the beginning. It did not attract or repel the paper. The pieces of paper were not charged because they were not attracted or repelled by the comb.
2. No; the charges in the comb are attracted to opposite charges in the paper.

Quick Lab

Sparks Are Flying

Unlocking the Key Concept

This activity will help students understand how static electricity builds up and is transferred.

Inquiry Focus

Develop a Hypothesis—suggesting a possible explanation about how electric charges build up and are transferred

Group Size Pairs or groups

Class Time 10 minutes

Advance Preparation

You might want to prepare the aluminum plates in advance by putting the handles on them.

Alternative Materials

Instead of rubbing the foam plate on your head, a wool scarf may be used or a piece of animal fur, such as rabbit. Foam trays used to package meat or produce may be used instead of round paper plates.

Procedure Tips

Perform this activity on a dry day. Performing it in a darkened room will be visually exciting.

Answers

1. Students should observe that each time they touch the pie plate, a spark is seen. The spark is a tiny amount of electrons, and is safe.
2. Sample Answer: When the pie plate is first put onto the foam, electrons in the foam repel electrons in the plate. Touching the plate causes a spark as electrons jump from the plate to the hand. Touching it again causes a spark as electrons jump back from the hand to the plate.
3. Sample Answer: Your hand provided a path for some charges to go into you or back to the plate.

Electric Current

Answering the Big Question

The activities in this lesson will help students answer the Big Question by having them describe how electric current is produced, explain the difference between insulators and conductors, and model potential difference.

Inquiry Warm-Up

How Can Current Be Measured?

Inquiry Focus

Predict—using observations and prior knowledge to predict how the makeup of a circuit affects the amount of current flowing through it

Group Size Pairs or groups

Class Time 15 minutes

Advance Preparation

Remove the insulation from the ends of the wire before conducting this experiment. Once stripped, the wires can be stored ready to use.

Procedure Tips

1. Demonstrate how to connect the batteries and then how to rewire the circuit in Step 6 each time a bulb and a socket are removed.
2. Suggest that the compass be connected last so the students can observe the movement of the needle.

Answers

1. The needle moved the most when no bulbs were present.
2. Light bulbs make it difficult for current to flow. Increasing the light bulbs in a circuit decreases the amount of current.

Quick Lab

Producing Electric Current

Unlocking the Key Concept

This activity will help students understand the requirements necessary to cause an electric current to flow.

Inquiry Focus

Form an Operational Definition—suggesting a possible set of requirements that allow an electric current to flow

Group Size Pairs or groups

Class Time 10 minutes

Advance Preparation

Cut wire into 25-cm lengths. Strip the insulation from the ends.

Alternative Materials

2 D-cells and a battery holder with a 2.8–3-V lamp can be substituted for the 1.5-V battery and associated components.

Answers

1. Look for answers that show an understanding of circuits and the need for complete circuits in order for an electric current to flow.
2. With only one side attached the circuit was open, not complete, so no electric current flowed.
3. Sample Answer: The light went out with the short circuit. The short circuit allowed current to bypass the light bulb.

Quick Lab

Conductors and Insulators

Unlocking the Key Concept

This activity will help students understand the properties of conductors and insulators.

Inquiry Focus

Predict—using prior knowledge to make predictions about what materials are insulators and conductors and then testing those predictions

Group Size Pairs or groups

Class Time 10 minutes

Advance Preparation

Cut wire into lengths and remove the insulation from the ends.

Alternative Materials

An aluminum foil strip may be used in place of aluminum wire.

Procedure Tips

The wire from the light and the one from the battery could be attached to brads placed a few cm apart on a piece of cardboard. Students then would need to only hold the test material across the two brads to test whether it is a conductor or an insulator, rather than connect them each time.

Answers

1. Student answers will vary depending on their predictions. Sample Answer: Conductors: copper and aluminum wire; Insulators: string and rubber band
2. Conductors: penny; Insulators: tire, scarf
3. Look for answers that show an understanding of how insulation works. Insulation keeps the conductors from touching and it prevents accidental contact with other conductors of electricity.

Quick Lab

Modeling Potential Difference

Unlocking the Key Concept

This activity will help students understand how potential difference increases and decreases.

Inquiry Focus

Make Models—creating a physical representation of potential difference

Group Size Pairs

Class Time 15 minutes

Procedure Tips

1. Check student plans, then have them test their models. A sample model might be to insert tubing through the bottom of the bottle, seal around the tubing with modeling clay, and fill the bottle with water.
2. Have paper towels on hand to clean up any spills or leaks.

Answers

1. The height is like a difference in potential, or potential difference.
2. As the bottle is raised, or the end of the tube is lowered, the water flows faster and faster, modeling a larger potential difference.
3. Look for answers that explain there must be a difference between the two end points, whether it is height, diameter, etc. When the end of the plastic tube is at the same height as the top of the water bottle, no water flows because there is no potential difference.

Electric Circuits

Answering the Big Question

The activities in this lesson will help students answer the Big Question by having them develop an understanding of series and parallel circuits and explore Ohm's law.

Inquiry Warm-Up

Do the Lights Keep Shining?

Inquiry Focus

Observe—using senses to gather and record information about how lights in series and parallel circuits behave when one light is removed

Group Size Pairs or groups

Class Time 15 minutes

Advance Preparation

Cut the wire into 25-cm lengths and remove the insulation from the ends.

Alternative Materials

A 6-V lantern battery may be substituted for the batteries and holder. However, be certain you use 6-V lights then or the bulbs will burn out.

Procedure Tips

You may want to have students include a switch in their circuits. If so, add it to one of the wires attached to the batteries.

Answers

1. In circuit 1 (the series), the remaining bulb went out. In circuit 2 (parallel), the remaining bulb remained lit.
2. Sample Answer: In circuit 1, the electric current stopped because there was only one path through which it could run. In the other circuit there was a second path for the current to flow through so the light stayed lit.
3. In both circuits, if the other light bulb was unscrewed the results would be the same.

Quick Lab

Ohm's Law

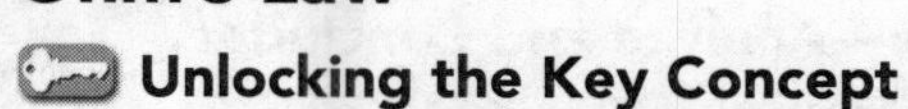

Unlocking the Key Concept

This activity will help students understand Ohm's law.

Inquiry Focus

Observe—using senses to gather information about how the intensity of light varies as a circuit's resistance is changed

Group Size Groups

Class Time 15 minutes

Advance Preparation

Carpenter pencils work well. Prepare the cut pencils in advance. Cut the pencils lengthwise with a utility knife or razor blade, trimming away enough wood to expose the graphite.

Alternative Materials

A graphite rod can be used instead of a pencil.

Procedure Tips

The wire or alligator clip needs to continuously touch the pencil graphite when it is moved up and down the pencil.

Answers

1. The light bulb became dimmer.
2. by moving the unattached alligator clip down the pencil, away from the other clip
3. Sample Answer: A dimmer switch probably works by increasing the resistance to dim the light, and decreasing the resistance to make it brighter.

Lab Investigation

Build a Flashlight

Unlocking the Key Concept

Both Versions This activity will help students develop an understanding of series and parallel circuits.

Answers—Pre Lab

Both Versions:

1. Series; the voltage will be higher.
2. The current will increase as resistance drops.

Answers—Do the Math

0.3 A or 300 mA, $I = V/R = 3.0\ V/10\ \Omega = 0.30\ A$

Inquiry Focus

Directed Inquiry:

Predict—utilizing knowledge of electric circuits to assemble circuits and predict the brightness of the resulting lit bulbs

Open Inquiry:

Make Models—designing and building a flashlight

Draw Conclusions—determining how batteries, wires, and a light bulb are best assembled to produce light

Group Size

Directed Inquiry Pairs or groups

Open Inquiry Pairs

Class Time

Both Versions 40 minutes

Safety

Both Versions:

1. Remind students to be careful when using scissors.
2. Make sure they wear safety goggles throughout the lab.

3. Caution students to handle glass bulbs gently, as broken bulbs can produce serious cuts.
4. Inform students that wiring voltage sources in parallel is dangerous.

Advance Preparation

Have students collect and bring in cardboard tubes from paper towels and/or bathroom tissue. It may be helpful to have several different types of commercial flashlights available for students to examine.

Alternative Materials

Directed Inquiry:

1. Small strands of home Christmas lights are a useful inexpensive substitute for light bulbs and sockets. When several bulbs fail, the strand is often thrown away, but most of the bulbs will still be good. Using wire cutters, individual lights and sockets may be cut out and the ends of the wire insulation then removed. Each bulb typically uses 2.5–3.0 volts.
2. Aluminum foil baking cups (for cupcakes) may be used instead of having students make reflectors.

Procedure Tips

Directed Inquiry:

1. It may be helpful to have a demonstration set of materials set out showing a light bulb in a reflector cup, a battery with wires taped to it, and the switch arrangement on the outside of a cardboard tube.
2. Have one or more examples of a store purchased flashlight available for students to observe.
3. If the bulb does not light, check to see that the connections are making firm contact. Test the bulb to be certain it is not burned out. Test the battery to make sure it can light the bulb. The light will be dim with one battery.

Open Inquiry:

1. Make sure students can identify all the components needed to construct a complete circuit. If they have made a complete circuit and the bulb still will not light, check to see that the connections are making firm contact. Test the bulb to be certain it is not burned out. Test the battery to make sure it is not drained.
2. Check that students' designs include a complete circuit and a reflector around the bulb. Refer to the direct inquiry version of this lab for one possible setup.
3. Sample Answer to Procedure Step 3: The bulb lit when we used the wires to form a complete circuit. One wire led from one end of the battery to the side of the base of the light bulb, and then another wire led from the center of the base of the bulb back to the other end of the battery.

Sample Data

Directed Inquiry:

Number of Lights and Batteries	Observations
One light, one battery	The bulb lights dimly.
One light, two batteries in series	The bulb is bright (brighter than before with one battery).
Two lights in parallel, two batteries in series	Both lights are bright.
Two lights in series, two batteries in series	Both bulbs light but dimly.

Answers—Analyze and Conclude

Directed Inquiry:

1. Look for answers that explain that three bulbs will use more current and will use up the battery quicker.
2. Sample Answer: The aluminum foil is the reflector for the flashlight. It reflects some of the light out the front of the flashlight for better illumination.
3. No; the orientation of the battery affects only the direction of the current. The light bulb will work with current flowing in either direction.
4. Sample Answer: If I increase the battery voltage, the light will be brighter.
5. Sample Answer: In a commercial flashlight, there is a permanent switch that is easy to operate, the case is plastic or metal, and the bulb can be easily removed or replaced.

Open Inquiry:

1. Sample Answer: I used the aluminum foil as the reflector for the flashlight. It reflects some of the light forward for better illumination. A curved mirror might be better used for this purpose.

2. Look for answers that state that it does not matter which battery terminals the wires are connected to; the bulb will light when current is flowing in either direction.
3. Look for answers that indicate that a complete circuit must include the bulb filament, so the bulb must be connected at both contact points.
4. Sample Answer: To make a brighter bulb, I could add more batteries or use a different type of bulb. To make the flashlight stronger, I could use a plastic or metal case instead of the cardboard tube.

Answers—Post Lab

Directed Inquiry:

1. Sample Answer: In order to make the bulbs brighter the voltage must be increased. Add more batteries to our cardboard tube. Another way is to replace the bulb with one requiring a smaller voltage.
2. Because the lights in series were dimmer, less current was flowing so the overall resistance was higher.
3. Students should summarize that lights in series will have less current flowing through them compared to the same bulbs wired in parallel. They may also comment on batteries that are wired in series increase the potential difference. Students might express a desire to learn more about larger parallel and series circuits or circuits they encounter in real life.

Communicate—The advertisements should include a description of how the flashlight works, and special features such as batteries and light bulbs in series or parallel.

Open Inquiry:

1. Sample Answer: A manufactured flashlight has a permanent switch that is easy to operate; the case is plastic or metal; the bulb can be easily removed and replaced. Commercial flashlights must be durable and reliable and operate in a variety of situations.
2. Sample Answer: With a tube-shaped flashlight, it is easy to aim the light. A tube shape is not the only possibility. This design can be improved upon by making the flashlight into a headlamp, with the light in front of the head and the battery behind so that it doesn't obstruct the view.
3. Sample Answer: I've learned that although they seem complex, most flashlights consist mainly of one simple circuit. I still want to know how to best use mirrors and lenses to intensify the light of a flashlight.

Communicate—Student advertisements should clearly show each part of the flashlight and indicate the function of each part. In addition, the advertisement should explain to potential customers the advantages of purchasing this flashlight.

Electric Power and Safety

Answering the Big Question

The activities in this lesson will help students answer the Big Question by having them explore how electric power is produced and increased and by having them calculate power and energy.

Inquiry Warm-Up

How Can You Make a Bulb Burn More Brightly?

Inquiry Focus

Pose Questions—stating a problem in a way that allows constructing an experiment or refining and refocusing questions about how to make a generator burn a light brighter

Group Size Pairs or groups

Class Time 15 minutes

Advance Preparation

Prepare the wires by removing insulation from the ends.

Alternative Materials

A bicycle generator with lights may be used instead of the hand crank generator.

Procedure Tips

Test your bulb in advance to determine how rapidly students can crank the generator without burning out the bulb. A 6-V bulb will get bright, but should not burn out. A 2.8–3.0-V bulb will probably burn out if students crank the generator too fast.

Answers

1. Sample Answer: The faster the generator was cranked, the brighter the bulb became. The more electrical energy provided, the brighter a bulb can burn.
2. Without a light bulb the generator is very easy to crank.
3. Sample Answer: Will the lights be as bright? Will all of the lights be the same brightness? Will I have to crank harder? Will the generator work with four lights?

Quick Lab

Calculating Electric Power and Energy Use

Unlocking the Key Concept

This activity will help students understand how to calculate power and energy for a light bulb in a circuit.

Inquiry Focus

Calculate—using mathematical processes to determine power and energy use of a light bulb in a circuit

Group Size Pairs

Class Time 20 minutes

Alternative Materials

A computer simulation of a circuit that allows for varying resistance could be substituted for the actual set-up.

Procedure Tips

Have a sample circuit set up for students to observe. Demonstrate the procedure of touching the probe to different points on the pencil lead. Set the ammeter/voltmeter between 10 and 20 amps.

Sample Data

See the sample data table on the following page.

Answers

1. Power output should increase. As power output increased, the bulb got brighter.
2. Sample Answer: Assume the D-cell has a standard voltage of 1.5 V.
3. Students should multiply the power output at one point by sixty seconds. This will be the energy used in Joules. For example, at the alligator clip, the current is .38 amps. The kW value is $1.5 \times .38 \div 1000 = .00057$kW. So the energy used after 60 seconds is equal to $.00057 \times 60\text{s} = .0342$kWsec.

Quick Lab

Electric Shock and Short Circuit Safety

Unlocking the Key Concept

This activity will help students understand one method of protecting people from electrical shocks and short circuits.

Inquiry Focus

Make Models—making a working model of an electrical safety device

Group Size Groups

Class Time 15 minutes

Advance Preparation

1. Prepare the steel wool strands in advance and stick them to masking tape.
2. Be sure students remove the strands from the masking tape before touching the ends together.

Procedure Tips

Build a circuit for students to use as an example.

Answers

1. Sample Answer: The light bulb lit up because touching the free ends together completed the circuit.
2. Sample Answer: The light bulb lit up at first because the circuit was complete, but the steel wool strand soon burned up and this interrupted the circuit so the bulb went out.
3. a fuse

Data Table—Calculating Electric Power and Energy Use

Distance from the probe & Alligator clip (mm)	Current (amps)	Brightness of the bulb	Power output of the bulb (W)
18	0.04	No light	.06
17.5	0.06	No light	.09
17.0	0.06	No light	.09
16.5	0.07	No light	.11
16.0	0.07	No light	.11
15.5	0.07	No light	.11
15.0	0.07	No light	.11
14.5	0.08	No light	.12
14.0	0.08	No light	.12
13.5	0.08	No light	.12
13.0	0.09	No light	.14
12.5	0.09	No light	.14
12.0	0.09	No light	.14
11.5	0.09	No light	.14
11.0	0.10	No light	.15
10.5	0.10	No light	.15
10.0	0.11	No light	.17
9.5	0.11	No light	.17
9.0	0.12	No light	.18
8.5	0.12	No light	.18
8.0	0.12	No light	.18
7.5	0.13	No light	.20
7.0	0.13	No light	.20
6.5	0.14	No light	.21
6.0	0.15	No light	.23
5.5	0.16	No light	.24
5.0	0.17	No light	.26
4.5	0.18	No light	.27
4.0	0.19	No light	.29
3.5	0.20	Very dim light	.30
3.0	0.21	Brighter Light	.32
2.5	0.22	Brighter Light	.33
2.0	0.23	Brighter Light	.35
1.5	0.24	Brighter Light	.36
1.0	0.25	Brighter Light	.38
.50	0.26	Brighter Light	.39
0 (touching the clip)	0.38	Very Bright Light	.57

Name ______________________ Date ____________ Class ____________

Inquiry Warm-Up

Can You Move a Can Without Touching It?

Have you ever wished that you could pull an object toward yourself without touching it? In this activity, you will use static electricity and observe what happens when objects that are statically charged interact with each other.

INQUIRY FOCUS Infer

Procedure

1. Place an empty aluminum can on its side on the floor.
2. Blow up the balloon and tie it closed. Then rub the balloon back and forth on your hair, shirt, pants, or sweater several times.
3. Hold the balloon about 2 to 3 cm away from the can.
4. Slowly move the balloon farther away from the can. Observe what happens.
5. Move the balloon to the other side of the can and observe what happens.

Materials

empty aluminum can
balloon

Think It Over

1. From your observations, what can you infer about the relationship between the can and the balloon?

____

____

2. In order to cause the can to start moving, what must be acting on it?

____

____

3. Moving the can required work. Recall that energy is the ability to do work or cause change. Can you infer where the source of energy came from to move the can?

____

____

Name ______________________ Date __________ Class __________

Quick Lab

Drawing Conclusions

Have you seen clothes sticking to each other from static electricity as they are removed from a clothes dryer? In this activity, you will observe the effect of bringing a charged object near an uncharged object.

INQUIRY FOCUS Draw Conclusions

Procedure

1. Tear the tissue paper into small pieces, about the size of a pencil eraser, or use a hole punch to cut circles.
2. Hold the comb near the pieces of paper. Observe what happens.
3. Run the comb through your hair several times, or rub it back and forth on your pants or shirt.
4. Place the comb close to, but not touching, the tissue paper pieces. Observe what happens,

Materials

tissue paper
hole punch
plastic comb

Think It Over

1. At the beginning of the lab, was the comb charged? Were the pieces of paper charged? How can you tell?

____

____

____

2. Did you do anything to charge the tissue? What can you conclude about the electric charges in the comb and in the tissue paper?

____

____

____

Name ______________________ Date ____________ Class ____________

Quick Lab — 10 min

Sparks Are Flying

Have you ever been shocked after sliding your feet across a carpet and then touching a door knob? Buildup of charges on an object is called static electricity. In this activity, you will generate static electricity.

INQUIRY FOCUS **Develop a Hypothesis**

Procedure

1. Cut a 3-cm wide strip from the middle of a foam plate. Fold the strip to form a "winged" V like the one shown in the diagram. Tape the wings to the center of the aluminum pie plate to make a handle.
2. Rub a second foam plate on your dry hair. Place it charged side up on the table.
3. Use the handle to pick up the pie plate. Hold the pie plate about 30 cm over the foam plate and drop it.
4. Now, very slowly, touch the tip of your finger to the pie plate. Be careful not to touch the foam plate. Then take your finger away.
5. Use the handle to pick up the pie plate again. Slowly touch the pie plate again.

Materials

- 2 foam plates
- tape
- scissors
- aluminum pie plate

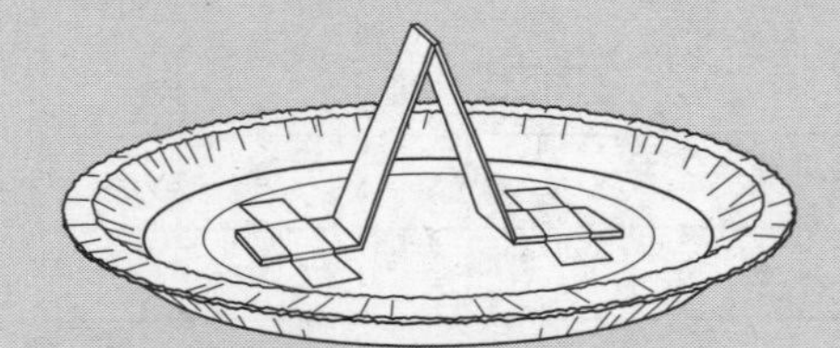

Think It Over

1. What did you observe each time you touched the pie plate?

____

____

2. How can you explain your observations?

____

____

3. What purpose may your hand have played when it touched the pie plate?

____

____

Name ______________________ Date ____________ Class ____________

Inquiry Warm-Up

How Can Current Be Measured?

Electric current is the flow of charges through a wire or device in a circuit. In this activity, you will develop knowledge of how to use a compass needle to measure electric current.

INQUIRY FOCUS Predict

Procedure

1. Obtain four pieces of wire, each about 25 cm long.
2. Wrap one of the wires four times around the compass. You may use a piece of tape to keep the wires in place. Make sure the compass needle can be seen.
3. Build a circuit using the remaining wire, wrapped compass, two bulbs, and a D-cell as shown in the figure. Make sure the compass is level. If it is not, place it on a piece of modeling clay so that the needle swings freely.
4. Adjust the compass position so that the wire is aligned directly over the compass needle.
5. Observe the compass needle as you complete the circuit. Using your protractor, measure the number of degrees the needle moves.
6. Repeat the activity using only one bulb, and again with no bulb.

Materials

- 1 m bell wire
- magnetic compass
- metric ruler
- modeling clay
- 2 1.5-V light bulbs and sockets
- electrical tape
- protractor
- D-cell and battery holder

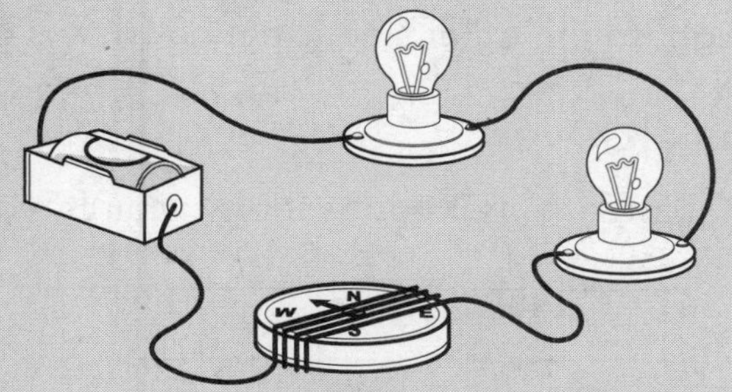

Think It Over

1. When did the compass needle move the most?

____

____

2. If four lights were wired together as the two had been, what movement of the compass needle would you expect? Explain.

____

____

____

Name ______________________ Date ______________ Class ______________

Quick Lab

Producing Electric Current

Electric current does not automatically flow from a battery. The current needs a specific path. In this activity, you will investigate how an electric current is made to flow.

INQUIRY FOCUS Form an Operational Definition

Procedure

1. Place the battery in the battery holder. Attach a wire from the positive end (+) of the battery holder to the light socket. Observe the light. Disconnect the wire.
2. Attach a wire from the negative end (−) of the battery holder to the light socket. Observe the light. Leave this wire connected.
3. Attach a wire from the positive end (+) of the battery holder to the other side of the light socket. Observe the light. Leave this wire connected.
4. Momentarily touch a third wire from the electrical connection on one side of the light to the other side, creating what is called a "short circuit." Observe the light.

Materials

- 1.5-V battery
- battery holder
- 1.5–2.0-V bulb
- light socket
- 3 25-cm lengths of bell wire

Think It Over

1. Based on your observations, what is required to cause an electrical current to flow?

____

____

2. Why did the bulb not light with only one side of the battery attached?

____

____

____

3. What did you observe with the short circuit?

____

____

____

Name ______________________ Date ____________ Class ____________

Quick Lab

Conductors and Insulators

Conductors are materials that current easily flows through while insulators are materials through which current cannot flow. In this activity, you will explore electrical conductors and insulators.

INQUIRY FOCUS Predict

Procedure

1. Look at the materials. Predict which materials should conduct electricity and which should be insulators.

   ____

   ____

2. Using two bell wires, attach one wire from the positive terminal of the the battery to the light bulb socket. Attach a second wire from the negative terminal of the battery to the other side of the light socket. Observe the light.
3. Disconnect one wire from the light. Attach a piece of aluminum wire between this end of the bell wire and the light. Observe the bulb.
4. Replace the aluminum wire with a copper wire and observe the light.
5. Repeat the process using a rubber band and a piece of string.

Materials

rubber band
10-cm string
10-cm copper wire
10-cm aluminum wire
2 25-cm lengths of bell wire
D-cell and battery holder
1.5-V light bulb
light bulb socket

Think It Over

1. Did your observations in Steps 2–5 support your predictions from Step 1? Explain.

   ____

   ____

2. Based on your results, predict whether a tire, a scarf, and a penny would be conductors or insulators.

   ____

   ____

3. Why do extension cords have rubber or plastic material covering them?

   ____

   ____

Name ________________ Date ________ Class ________

Quick Lab

15 min 

Modeling Potential Difference

Potential difference, or voltage, is the difference in the electric potential energy per charge between two different points in a circuit. In this activity, you will use water to model potential difference.

INQUIRY FOCUS **Make Models**

Procedure

1. Using the materials provided, design and build a model that can represent what happens as voltage, or potential difference, increases. Draw your plan to model potential difference in the space below.
2. Have your teacher check your plans and, after receiving approval, build and test your model.
3. Observe the water output as you move the open end of the tubing higher and lower.

Materials

plastic bottle with small hole in the bottom and cap removed
flexible plastic tubing
basin
modeling clay

Think It Over

1. How did your model represent voltage?

____

2. How did changing the height of the open tube affect the model's voltage?

____

3. If there is no difference in height of the water and the open end of the tube, what difference in potential exists?

____

Name ________________________ Date ____________ Class ____________

Inquiry Warm-Up

Do the Lights Keep Shining?

Electric current must have a complete circuit in order to flow. Circuits can be either series circuits or parallel circuits. In this activity, you will build two types of circuits and observe what happens to the lights as some are unscrewed.

INQUIRY FOCUS Observe

Procedure

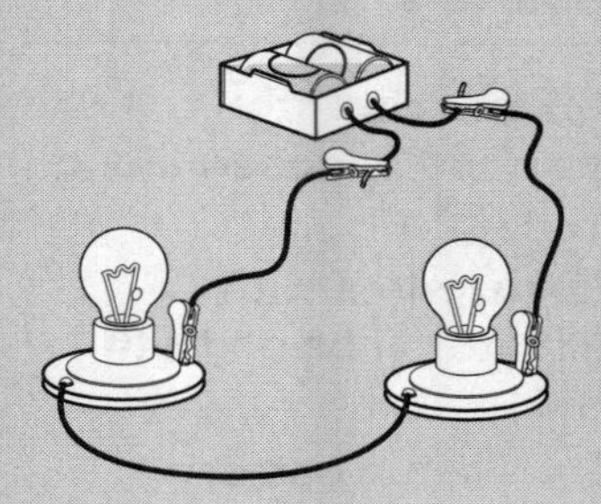

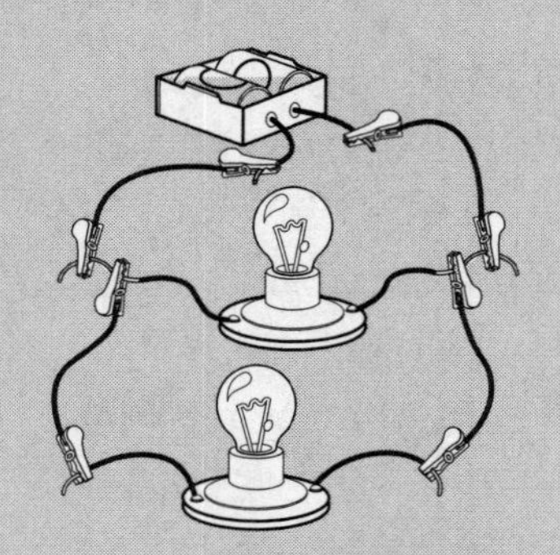

Materials

- 4 light bulbs with sockets
- 4 D-cell batteries with battery holders
- several 25-cm lengths of insulated wire
- 12 alligator clips

1. Construct both of the circuits shown using a battery, several insulated wires, and two light bulbs for each circuit.
2. Connect all of the wires and observe the lights.
3. Now, unscrew one bulb in each circuit and observe the remaining bulbs.

Think It Over

1. What happened to the remaining light bulb in each circuit when you unscrewed one bulb?

____

____

2. How can you account for your observations?

____

____

3. Predict what would happen if you screwed the loose bulb back in, and unscrewed the other bulb in each circuit.

____

____

Name ________________________ Date____________ Class____________

Quick Lab — 15 min

Ohm's Law

The length of a conductor affects the amount of current flowing in a circuit. Recall that Ohm's law states that voltage equals current times the resistance in the circuit. In this activity, you will observe Ohm's law in action.

INQUIRY FOCUS Observe

Procedure

1. Construct a circuit by connecting one end of the first wire to the positive terminal of the battery and the other end of the same wire to the graphite of the pencil.
2. Use a second wire to connect the negative terminal of the battery to one of the light socket terminals.
3. Attach one end of the third wire to the vacant light socket terminal. Leave the other end of the third wire unattached.
4. Touch the unattached end of the third wire to the graphite near the point where the first wire is attached to the graphite. Observe the light bulb.
5. Slowly slide the same free end down the length of the graphite, moving away from the attached alligator clip toward the other end of the pencil. Observe the light bulb.

Materials

- No. 2 pencil, with graphite exposed along its length
- 3 25-cm wires with alligator clips on both ends
- 2 D-cells in a battery holder
- 3-V light bulb in a socket

Think It Over

1. What did you observe about the intensity of the light as the unattached alligator clip was moved down the pencil, away from the other clip?

____

____

2. How were you able to increase the resistance in your circuit?

____

____

3. Given what you observed, how do you think a dimmer switch might work?

____

____

____

Name ______________________ Date ____________ Class ____________

PRE LAB

Build a Flashlight

Reviewing Content

Series or parallel circuits are two ways to have devices hooked together in an electric circuit.

If all of the parts of an electric circuit are connected in a single path, the circuit is a series circuit. If all of the parts of the circuit are on separate branches so the current can take a different path, then the arrangement is a parallel circuit. In a series circuit, the same current passes through each part. In a parallel circuit different amounts of current can pass through each branch.

Using Ohm's law, V=IR, you can calculate the amount of current that passes through a light bulb. For example, a light bulb with a resistance of 10 Ω is hooked to a potential difference of 1.5 volts. The amount of current is equal to:

$I = \frac{V}{R} = \frac{1.5\ V}{10\ \Omega} = 0.15\ A.$

As more current flows through a light bulb, the bulb becomes brighter.

In this lab, you will investigate and describe the basic features of series and parallel circuits as you build a flashlight.

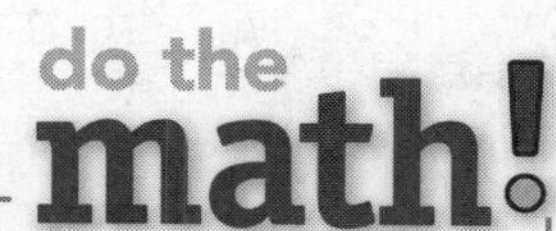

What current flows through a light bulb having a resistance of 10 Ω when a potential difference of 3.0 Volts is applied to it?

Reviewing Inquiry Focus

When you make predictions you are using your prior experience or knowledge to make an educated guess about some future event that you will be testing. You have likely used a flashlight at some time in your life. How did the batteries fit in the flashlight? Did you know if the flashlight would light when you changed the batteries? Based on your previous experience with flashlights, you were probably able to predict that the flashlight bulb would light when the batteries were inserted in a certain way. Preview the Lab Investigation. Then answer the questions.

1. Will a series circuit or parallel circuit provide a brighter lit bulb?

   ____

   ____

2. As more light bulbs are wired in parallel, the net resistance decreases in the circuit. What will happen to the amount of current flowing from the batteries?

   ____

   ____

Name ______________________ Date ______________ Class ______________

DIRECTED Inquiry

Build a Flashlight

Problem

How can you build a working flashlight?

INQUIRY FOCUS
Predict

Materials

2 3-V light bulbs in sockets
2 D-cell batteries, 1.5-V
cardboard tube
paper cup
aluminum foil
screwdriver
duct tape
scissors
5 lengths of wire, about 15 cm each, with the insulation stripped off about 2 cm from each end
1 length of wire, 15–20 cm long with the insulation stripped off each end.

Procedure

1. Make two holes in the side of the tube, about 3–4 cm apart. The holes should be in the middle of the tube.
2. Use duct tape to connect a 10-cm wire to each terminal of one battery.
3. Using a pencil, punch a hole in the middle of the bottom of the paper cup. The hole should be about the size of the base of the light bulb. Line the paper cup with aluminum foil.
4. Attach two short wires to the light bulb socket base. Insert the light bulb up through the bottom of the cup so that the socket is below the cup.
5. Pass the light socket wires into the cardboard tube. Push one through the top hole you made in the tube. Attach the other light socket wire to the wire coming from the positive terminal of the battery. Place a piece of tape over this connection to cover the wire. Take a new wire and feed its end up from the bottom of the tube and out of the bottom hole in the cardboard tube. Attach this wire to the tube with a piece of tape to prevent it from sliding out of the tube.
6. Attach the paper cup onto the top of the cardboard tube with a piece of tape. Slide the battery into the bottom of the cardboard tube. Attach the wire on the negative terminal of the battery to the wire sticking out the bottom of the tube.
7. Touch the two free ends of the wires coming from the holes together and see if the bulb lights. Observe your light. Turn the light off. These wires act as the switch of your flashlight. Record your observations in the data table on the next page.
8. Prepare a second battery as you did in Step 2. Carefully disconnect the long wire coming from your switch out the bottom of your tube from the bottom of the battery.

9. Attach the wire from the top of the *second* battery to the wire from the bottom of the first battery. Reattach the long switch wire to the bottom of the second battery. You now have two batteries in series. Place tape over the wire connections. Carefully slide the second battery into the tube.

10. Touch the two free ends of the switch wires coming from the holes together and see if the bulb lights. Observe your light. Turn the light off. Record your observations in the table.

11. Construct a second paper cup reflector with a light bulb socket. Remove the first cup from your tube by gently pulling on the tape. Attach the wires from the new socket to the socket of the first light by placing one on one side and the other on the opposite side, making a parallel light setup. Tape the two lights to the cardboard tube.

12. Turn on your light by connecting the switch wires. Observe the lights. Turn off the lights. Record your observations in the table.

13. Carefully remove the lights from the end of the tube. Disconnect the second light from the flashlight, but leave one wire attached to the socket. Disconnect one wire from the first light at the socket, but leave the other end attached to the flashlight. Attach this wire to the empty connection of the second light socket. Connect the loose wire from the second socket to the empty connection on the first light socket. The lights are now in series.

14. Turn on the light switch and observe the lights. Record your observations in the table.

Data Table

Number of Lights and Batteries	Observations
One light, one battery	
One light, two batteries in series	
Two lights in parallel, two batteries in series	
Two lights in series, two batteries in series	

Analyze and Conclude

1. **Predict** Would a flashlight with three bulbs wired in parallel last as long as a flashlight having only one bulb? Explain.

2. **Infer** What is the purpose of lining the cups with aluminum foil?

3. **Draw Conclusions** Does it matter which way the battery is placed in the tube? Explain.

4. **Develop a Hypothesis** How could you make your flashlight brighter?

5. **Evaluate the Design** Compare your flashlight to a manufactured one. Explain the difference.

Name ______________________ Date ____________ Class ____________

DIRECTED Inquiry ● Lab Investigation

POST LAB

Build a Flashlight

1 **Infer** If you wanted to leave the lights in series, as they were in the final setup of the lab, what could be done to make them brighter?

____

____

____

____

2 **Interpret Data** Using your observations of the lights in series, what was the overall circuit resistance compared with having only one light?

____

____

____

____

3 **Summarize** Summarize what you have learned about light circuits in parallel and series. List any questions that you still have.

What I learned ____

____

____

____

What I still want to know ____

____

____

____

Communicate

Demonstrate Consumer Literacy Write an advertisement for your flashlight. In your ad, list the features of your flashlight, and explain why a consumer should buy it.

Name ______________________ Date ______________ Class ______________

OPEN Inquiry

Build a Flashlight

Problem

How can you build a working flashlight?

INQUIRY FOCUS
Make Models, Draw Conclusions

Materials

cardboard tube
D-cell battery
flashlight bulb
aluminum foil
paper cup
duct tape
scissors
2 lengths of wire, about 10 cm each, with the insulation stripped off about 2 cm at each end
1 length of wire, 15–20 cm, with the insulation stripped off at each end

Design an Experiment

1. Imagine that a young child brings you a flashlight, turns it on, and says: "How does that happen?" You decide to build a flashlight to show the child how science makes the flashlight work.

2. Start by experimenting with the wires, battery, and flashlight bulb to see if you can get the bulb to light up. *Hint: Most bulbs have a bottom contact and a side contact. If there is no obvious side contact, try touching the metal on the side of the base.*

3. Record your observations of the setup that worked.

____

____

____

____

4. Now that you know how the wires, battery, and bulb can be used to produce light, design a flashlight using the rest of your materials. Draw your design in the space provided on the next page.

5. Have your teacher check and approve your design. Then build your flashlight.

Flashlight Design

Analyze and Conclude

1. **Make Models** How did you use the aluminum foil? What might be a better material for this purpose?

2. **Draw Conclusions** Does it matter which battery terminals the wires are connected to? Why or why not?

3. **Infer** Why does the bulb have to be connected at two points in order for it to light?

4. **Evaluate the Design** How could you make your flashlight brighter? How could you make it more sturdy?

Name ______________________ Date ____________ Class ____________

OPEN Inquiry — Lab Investigation

POST LAB

Build a Flashlight

1 **Observe** Compare your flashlight to a manufactured one. Explain the differences.

____

____

____

____

2 **Design a Solution** What are some advantages of a tube-shaped flashlight? Is a tube shape the only possible design for a flashlight? How could this design be improved upon?

____

____

____

____

____

3 **Summarize** Describe what you've learned about flashlights. List any questions that you still have.

What I learned

____

____

____

What I still want to know

____

____

____

Communicate

Demonstrate Consumer Literacy Write an advertisement for your flashlight. In your ad, list the features of your flashlight, and explain why a consumer should buy it.

Name ______________________ Date __________ Class __________

Inquiry Warm-Up

15 min

How Can You Make a Bulb Burn More Brightly?

A generator converts mechanical energy into electrical energy. In this activity, you are going to supply the mechanical energy by doing work to turn the handle of a generator in order to make a light bulb burn more brightly.

INQUIRY FOCUS Pose Questions

Procedure

1. Connect the two wires from the generator to the light bulb base connectors.
2. Slowly crank the generator. Observe the brightness of the bulb.
3. Crank the generator a little faster. Observe the bulb.
4. Crank the generator quickly. Observe the bulb.

Materials

light bulb in socket (3–6-V)

hand crank generator

1 m insulated copper wire

Think It Over

1. How does the speed at which you crank the generator affect the brightness of the bulb? Explain how the rate of generating electrical energy is related to the brightness of the bulb.

___

___

___

2. There is no load on the generator when the light bulb is unscrewed. How does the amount of effort necessary to crank it change?

___

___

3. If you hooked up three more light bulbs to your generator, what are two questions that you could explore?

___

___

___

Name ________________ Date ________ Class ________

Quick Lab

Calculating Electric Power and Energy Use

Electrical energy is measured in kilowatt-hours (kWh). In this activity, you will calculate your daily energy use.

INQUIRY FOCUS Calculate

Procedure

1. Connect two wires to each end of the battery. Clip the other end of one of these wires to one end of the pencil lead. Clip the end of the other wire to one of the connections of the light bulb holder.
2. Clip one end of the third wire to the other connection on the light bulb holder. Clip the other end of the third wire to one of the probes of the ammeter or multimeter. If using a multimeter, make sure it is set to display current.
3. Touch the free probe of the meter to different points on the pencil lead. Start as far from the alligator clip as possible, making each point 5 mm closer to the clip. For each point, record the distance between the probe and the alligator clip, the current reading on the meter, and whether the bulb gets brighter or dimmer.
4. On a sheet of paper, design a data table and record your data.

Materials

- thick mechanical pencil lead
- 2 D-cell batteries
- D-cell battery holder, double
- 1.5–2.0-V light bulb w/ holder
- 3 wires with alligator clips on each end
- ammeter or multimeter
- ruler
- white paper

Think It Over

1. Recall that power equals voltage times current. Does power output increase or decrease as current increases? Look at your data table. How does power output affect the brightness of the bulb?

   ____

   ____

   ____

2. Calculate the power output of the bulb for each data point you collected. Refer to your student edition for help and record the information in your data table.

Name ______________________ Date__________ Class__________

Quick Lab — 15 min

Electric Shock and Short Circuit Safety

Electrical safety at home and school is important. In this activity, you will model a common electrical safety device.

INQUIRY FOCUS Make Models

Materials

- 6-V battery
- 6.3-V bulb in bulb holder
- three wires with alligator clips at each end
- 2-cm long single strand of steel wool

Procedure

1. Attach one wire from one terminal of the battery to one terminal of the lamp holder. Attach the second wire to the other terminal of the battery and leave the other end of the wire unattached. Attach the third wire to the open terminal of the lamp holder and leave the other end of the wire unattached.
2. Touch the two free ends of the second and third wires together briefly. Observe what happens to the light bulb. Separate the ends of the second and third wires.
3. Clip the free end of the second wire to one end of the steel wool strand. Without touching the steel wool with your fingers, attach the free end of the third wire to the other end of the steel wool. Observe what happens.
4. Disconnect the wires from the battery.

Think It Over

1. What is the explanation for what you observed in Step 2?

____

____

2. Explain the reason you observed what you did in Step 3.

____

____

3. What kind of electrical safety device is modeled in this activity?

____

____

CHAPTER 7

TABLE OF CONTENTS

Magnetism and Electromagnetism

Teacher Notes 170

What Is Magnetism?

Inquiry Warm-Up	Natural Magnets		182
Lab Investigation	Detecting Fake Coins	*Pre Lab*	183
		Directed Inquiry	184
		Open Inquiry	188
Quick Lab	Magnetic Poles		192

Magnetic Fields

Inquiry Warm-Up	Predict the Field	193
Quick Lab	Spinning in Circles	194
Quick Lab	Earth's Magnetic Field	195

Electromagnetic Force

Inquiry Warm-Up	Electromagnetism	196
Quick Lab	Electric Current and Magnetism	197
Quick Lab	Magnetic Fields From Electric Current	198
Quick Lab	Electromagnet	199

Electricity, Magnetism, and Motion

Inquiry Warm-Up	How Are Electricity, Magnets, and Motion Related?	200
Quick Lab	Can a Magnet Move a Wire?	201
Quick Lab	How Galvanometers Work	202
Quick Lab	Parts of an Electric Motor	203

Electricity From Magnetism

Inquiry Warm-Up	Electric Current Without a Battery	204
Quick Lab	Inducing an Electric Current	205
Quick Lab	How Generators Work	206
Quick Lab	How Transformers Work	207

What Is Magnetism?

Answering the Big Question

The activities in this lesson will help students answer the Big Question by observing how a compass works, by using magnets, and by exploring the relationship between magnets and Earth's magnetic field.

Inquiry Warm-Up

Natural Magnets

Inquiry Focus

Observe—studying how a compass needle responds to different materials

Group Size Groups

Class Time 10 minutes

Safety

1. Magnets can affect the way certain electronic devices work. Caution students to keep the magnets away from their watches and computers in the room.
2. Students should handle the compasses carefully.

Procedure Tips

1. Label the rocks in some way, either with letters or by type of rock.
2. Instruct students to wait until the needle is still before testing a new rock.
3. The rocks should be placed somewhere away from the magnet when not being tested. Any type of rock can be used, but lodestone and/or magnetite should be included in the set because they will cause movement of the compass needle.

Answers

1. The compass needle moved. The lodestone and magnetite also caused the needle to move.
2. The paper clip would stick to the lodestone.
3. Sample Answer: The needles pointed in the same direction. The needles could be reacting to a magnet inside Earth.

Lab Investigation

Detecting Fake Coins

Unlocking the Key Concept

Both Versions This activity will show students how magnets can be used to differentiate between coins and magnetic metal objects.

Answers—Pre Lab

Both Versions:

1. Students may list properties of coins, such as size, shape, mass, density, and magnetic properties.
2. If the magnet were on the center line, it would only slow down the iron slugs and washers instead of deflecting them to one side.

Inquiry Focus

Directed Inquiry:

Predict—making an educated guess about the effect of a magnet on real and fake coins

Open Inquiry:

Observe—collecting data by watching what happens to coins and washers as they travel down a slide that is fitted with a magnet

Develop a Hypothesis—using observations and prior knowledge to make a prediction about how coins and steel washers will interact with a magnet

Group Size

Directed Inquiry Pairs or groups

Open Inquiry Groups

Class Time

Both Versions 40 minutes

Safety

Both Versions:

1. Caution students to keep watches and other electronic devices away from the magnets.
2. Review the Laboratory Safety Rules at the front of this book.

Advance Preparation (15 minutes)

Both Versions:

1. Check the strength of the bar magnets you have on hand.
2. Obtain an assortment of iron washers. Test the washers to make sure they are attracted to the magnets.

3. Collect the appropriate number of cardboard sheets, craft sticks, washers of various sizes, and small bar magnets.
4. Supply coins or have students bring their own.

Alternative Materials

Both Versions:

If you can obtain some Canadian coins, have students try them on the apparatus and note the results. Current Canadian denominations below one dollar are made from plated steel.

Procedure Tips

Directed Inquiry:

1. Use only bar magnets that are relatively strong.
2. One factor that can affect the effectiveness of students' devices is the angle of the inclined cardboard. When the angle is increased to more than 45°, the coins and washers will move down more quickly, decreasing the amount that a washer is deflected by the magnet.
3. Another factor to consider is the strength of the magnet. If a strong magnet is used, a steeper angle of incline may be needed. An alternative is to place the magnet farther than 2 cm from the center line.

Open Inquiry:

1. Begin by asking students to name some machines or devices that are coin-operated. Ask, **What is a slug?** *(a fake coin)* Ask, **What do you think happens with these machines if you put in a slug or a coin from another country?** *(The machine doesn't register the fake and spits it back out.)* Ask, **How is the machine able to tell the difference between a real coin and a slug or a foreign coin?** *(Students may list a variety of properties of the coins, such as shape, size, weight, magnetism.)* Lead the discussion towards magnetism. Ask, **Are coins magnetic?** *(no)* **How do magnets affect metal objects?** *(They either attract or repel iron-containing metal objects.)* **Could magnets be used in these machines to distinguish between real coins and fakes?** *(possibly)*
2. Distribute the cardboard, magnet, coins, washers and tape to each group. Offer any other materials that could be useful, such as rulers, craft sticks, tongue depressors, and straws.
3. Allow the students 10–15 minutes to come up with a design. Look over their procedures and designs and offer any guidance before they begin testing. Remind them if they run into trouble to refer to their list of troubleshooting questions (Step 7) and make adjustments based on its suggestions. Factors that could influence the effectiveness of their designs include:
   - **the angle of the inclined cardboard**—When the angle is more than 45°, the coins and washers will move more quickly, decreasing a washer's chance of being attracted to the magnet.
   - **the strength of the magnet**—If a strong magnet is used, a steeper angle of incline may be needed. An alternative is to place the magnet farther than 2 cm from the center line.
   - **the thickness of the cardboard**—If the cardboard is too thin, such as the type used in file folders, the washers will stick to the magnet. If the cardboard is too thick, the magnetism will be too weak to affect the washer. The ideal cardboard is the type used at the back of a legal pad of paper.
   - **the placement of the track**—If the directed path to separate the coins and washers is not close enough to the magnet (where the deflection will occur), the washers will not go down a separate path. The deflection track should be placed no more than 5 cm from where the bottom of the magnet would be.
4. Sample Hypothesis for Procedure Step 3: The coins will not be affected by the magnet, but the coins will be because they contain metals which are magnetic.

Answers—Analyze and Conclude

Directed Inquiry:

1. Sample Answer: The coins will slide straight down because they are not attracted by a magnet. The washers will slide straight until they are deflected because they are attracted to the magnet. Then they will slide along the stick.
2. Answers will depend on predictions. Students should see the coins slide straight down the cardboard while the washers veered off and slid along the stick.

3. Sample Answer: The magnet attracts any magnetic materials as they slide down the cardboard.
4. Look for answers that note the presence or absence of magnetic and nonmagnetic metals. For example, the coins are composed of non-magnetic metals, which a magnet does not attract. The washers are composed of magnetic metals, which a magnet does attract.
5. Sample Answer: The steepness of the cardboard affects the speed at which objects slide down the cardboard. When objects are moving slowly, that the magnet will attract and deflect objects made of magnetic materials more effectively. Some students might also mention that the strength of the magnet affects how steep the cardboard can be. A stronger magnet would allow for a steeper angle.
6. Sample Answer: The device would not be useful in Canada because Canadian coins are magnetic and would be attracted by the magnet, just as steel washers are attracted.

Open Inquiry:

1. Look for answers that indicate that the magnet serves as the separation device for the coins and the washers. The magnet separates the objects by whether or not they are attracted to the magnet.
2. Sample Answer: The coins slid straight down the cardboard. The metal washers zigzagged when they came near the magnet.
3. My hypothesis was supported because I predicted the coins would not be affected by the magnet and the washers would be.
4. Sample Answer: The angle of the cardboard, the thickness of the cardboard, the placement of the magnet, the distance of the track from the magnet, and the strength of the magnet were all factors we had to consider and adjust in order for our design to work.
5. Look for answers that have a second component of the design that separates coins from slugs based on an additional property of the coins, such as weight, density, or size.

Answers—Post Lab

Directed Inquiry:

1. Students should state that they saw the coins slide straight down the middle of the cardboard, but that the slugs were deflected to the side and rolled down the ramp made of the craft stick. The slugs were attracted by the magnet, but the coins were not.
2. Students may not know that aluminum and brass are non-magnetic. They know, however, that iron is magnetic.
3. Student summaries should show that they understand that real coins of the United States are not magnetic, and iron or steel slugs and washers are. Thus, the fake coins can be deflected by a magnet. Students may want to know what causes magnetism and why some things are affected by a magnet while others are not.

Communicate—In their brochures, students should explain the difference between materials that are magnetic and materials that are not. Students should also describe how the device uses that difference to separate coins from slugs.

Open Inquiry:

1. Sample Answer: We had to change the angle of the cardboard several times because the washers were going by the magnet either too slowly or too quickly and not separating from the coins. We also had to move the track a couple of times so that the washers were caught soon after the magnet deflected them.
2. Sample Answer: I would design a token that had no magnetic properties so it couldn't be distinguished from a regular coin.
3. Look for answers that describe situations where metal objects are being separated from non-metal or non-magnetic items. For example, food manufacturers use magnets to be sure that no metal parts from the machinery get into the food.
4. Student summaries should show that they understand that real coins of the United States are not magnetic, and iron and steel slugs and washers are. Thus, the fake coins can be deflected by a magnet. Students may want to know what causes magnetism and why some things are affected by a magnet while others are not.

Communicate—Students' presentations should demonstrate a clear understanding of how their machines use physical properties to separate coins, that their machines were adequately tested, and how magnetism separates real and fake coins.

Quick Lab

Magnetic Poles

Unlocking the Key Concept

This activity will help students understand how magnetic poles interact.

Inquiry Focus

Draw Conclusions—using observations of interacting magnets to make statements about the polarity of magnets

Group Size Groups

Class Time 15 minutes

Safety

1. Caution students to keep the magnets away from watches, computers, and other electrical devices.
2. Explain that magnets can lose some of their magnetism, and bar magnets can break into pieces if they are dropped. Remind students to handle the magnets carefully.

Procedure Tips

1. Before class, label the magnets. On two-thirds of the magnets, label the north pole with an "A" and the south pole with a "B." Leave one-third blank.
2. Demonstrate how hard the cars should be rolled toward each other.
3. If cars are unavailable, instruct students to place the magnets on the table facing each other and slowly bring the magnets toward each other.

Answers

1. Sides A and B have different polarities.
2. Sample Answer: When I rolled the car with the blank magnet toward the "B" side of a magnet, it was attracted. This means that the side facing forward must be the "A" side and the other side is the "B" side.
3. No. I would need a compass or a magnet with its poles labeled.

Magnetic Fields

Answering the Big Question

The activities in this lesson will help students answer the Big Question by having them visualize magnetic fields, observe how a compass works, and explore features of Earth's magnetic field.

Inquiry Warm-Up

Predict the Field

Inquiry Focus

Predict—suggesting a possible shape of the magnetic field around a magnet

Group Size Groups

Class Time 15 minutes

Safety

1. Students should wear their safety goggles throughout this activity.
2. Caution students not to open the containers or touch the iron filings.
3. Remind students to keep watches and other electronic devices away from the magnets.

Advance Preparation (10 minutes)

Gather several different-shaped magnets and distribute one magnet to each group.

Alternative Materials

Instead of using the petri dish, you can shake iron filings into any other clear and shallow container. Seal the container with a clear lid or clear tape.

Procedure Tips

1. Results will be better if students always make sure the iron filings are evenly distributed before testing a magnet; the filings should not all be bunched up in one part of the petri dish.
2. Have the students look at the side view of the iron filings as well as the view from overhead.
3. Sample Prediction for Procedure Step 1: The iron fillings will line up in the shape of the magnet.

Answers

1. Plastic shavings contain no iron and are not attracted to magnets.

2. Look for answers that state the force increases. The iron filings could get closer together where the magnetic force is stronger.

Quick Lab

Spinning in Circles

Unlocking the Key Concept

This activity will help students understand that a compass responds in the same way to any magnetic field whether produced by a small magnet or by Earth and that the magnetic field of a magnet may be visualized and mapped using a compass.

Inquiry Focus

Draw Conclusions—analyzing how the direction a compass needle points shows the general shape of the magnetic field surrounding the magnet, and making a statement about how a compass responds to the magnetic field of both a magnet and the magnetic field of Earth

Group Size Individuals or pairs

Class Time 10 minutes

Safety

1. Remind students to keep watches and other electronic devices away from the magnets.
2. Caution students that a magnet can break or become demagnetized if dropped.

Materials

1. Small diameter (about 1.5 cm) compasses are ideal, inexpensive, and available.
2. Bar magnets for the exercise should be about 10 to 20 times longer than they are wide, and preferably have labeled poles.

Advance Preparation (15 minutes)

1. Test the compasses to make sure they are in working order.
2. Test the magnets you will use to be sure they are still magnetized.

Alternative Materials

A long, small diameter, cylindrical magnet can substitute for the bar magnet.

Procedure Tips

Show students which end of the compass needle points north.

Answers

1. The pattern formed by the arrows represents the magnetic field surrounding the bar magnet.
2. Sample Answer: The arrows point directly toward or directly away from the poles but point parallel to the magnet at the halfway point.
3. Compasses respond both to Earth's magnetic field and to magnetic material near them.

Quick Lab

Earth's Magnetic Field

Unlocking the Key Concept

This activity will allow students to see the important features of Earth's magnetic field.

Inquiry Focus

Make Models—making a physical representation of Earth's magnetic field

Group Size Groups

Class Time 15 minutes

Safety

Students should wear their safety goggles throughout this activity.

Procedure Tips

1. Demonstrate how the vial should be positioned in the bottle.
2. To save time, you might wish to put the magnets in the test tubes and tie on the strings.

Answers

1. A side view of the Western Hemisphere; in Step 4, we saw a magnetic field where one pole was at the top of the field and the other pole was at the bottom, which is what you would see if you looked at the Western Hemisphere.
2. Sample Answer: It is stronger at the poles. The iron filings bunched up much more at the poles than in the middle of the bottle, showing that the magnetic field is stronger at the poles.

Electromagnetic Force

Answering the Big Question

The activities in this lesson will help students answer the Big Question by having them observe how an electric current produces a magnetic field that can affect a compass, examine the relationship between electric current and magnetism, and describe how electromagnets increase the magnetic field produced by moving charges.

Inquiry Warm-Up

Electromagnetism

Infer—suggesting a possible explanation for the behavior of a compass when the compass is placed close to a wire carrying electric current

Group Size Pairs or groups

Class Time 15 minutes

Advance Preparation (30 minutes)

1. Assemble one or more of the apparatus shown in student procedure. For each Oersted apparatus, you will need 2 insulated wires, 16–20-gauge (20–30 cm long); 1.5-V light bulb with bulb holder; D-cell battery (1.5-V) with battery holder; knife switch; wooden board (optional).
2. Check that the battery is not discharged and that the light bulb is working.
3. Make sure the compass needles turn freely.

Alternative Materials

A C-cell battery may be used in place of the D-cell battery. They are less expensive and more readily available.

Procedure Tips

1. You may want to construct one or two of the Oersted setups and place them as experiment stations. Have students rotate through the stations in pairs to conduct the experiment.
2. A poor connection to the battery or a loose bulb can cause the lamp not to light.

Answers

1. Sample Answer: The compass needles move when the switch is closed.
2. The light bulb lights.
3. Look for answers that make a connection between the electric current and its affect on a magnetic needle. For example, current in the wire creates a magnetic field that affects the compasses.

Quick Lab

Electric Current and Magnetism

Unlocking the Key Concept

This activity will help students understand the relationship between electric current and magnetism.

Inquiry Focus

Infer—making a statement about the relationship between the direction of an electric current and the magnetic field it creates

Group Size Groups

Class Time 10 minutes

Safety

1. Students should wear their safety goggles throughout this activity.
2. Remind students that the ends of the wires might be sharp.

Advance Preparation (15 minutes)

Use a large nail or sharpened pencil to make two holes in each box. The first hole should be in the center of the box top, and the other hole should be in one of the box sides.

Procedure Tips

Have a sample setup for students to look at. Tape the wire to the table at two points, about a third of the way in from either end, leaving the ends free enough to reach the terminals of the battery. It is important to secure the wire because students will not see the correct results if they flip the wire around instead of the battery.

Answers

1. The direction the current is flowing was changed.
2. The needle pointed in a different direction.
3. Sample Answer: The direction of an electric current affects the magnetic field it produces.

Quick Lab

Magnetic Fields From Electric Current

Unlocking the Key Concept

This activity will allow students to observe how an electric current creates its own magnetic field.

Inquiry Focus

Interpret Data—using drawings of the orientation of a compass needle to see the magnetic field pattern around the wire

Group Size Groups

Class Time 15 minutes

Safety

1. Remind students that the ends of the wires can be sharp.
2. Use the compasses with care.

Procedure Tips

1. A small box, like the kind jewelry comes in, is ideal. A paper cup will also work for this procedure if you have small compasses.
2. Have the holes in the boxes punched before the activity begins. The holes should be as small as possible; just large enough to thread the wire through.
3. If drawing compasses are not available, make a stencil of a circle 2 cm in diameter for the students to trace.

Answers

1. Sample Answer: The magnetic field goes in a circle around the wire.
2. They would stop forming a circle and all point toward the magnetic north pole.

Quick Lab

Electromagnet

Unlocking the Key Concept

This activity will help students understand that an electromagnet has properties similar to a permanent magnet when current is flowing through it but has no magnetic properties when there is no electric current.

Inquiry Focus

Infer—suggesting an explanation for the differences in the magnetic behavior of an electromagnet when electric current is flowing through the device and when there is no current

Group Size Individuals or pairs

Class Time 15 minutes

Safety

1. Remind students that the ends of the wire can be sharp.
2. The wire should be connected to the battery only long enough to observe the magnetic effect. Leaving it connected longer will deplete the battery and cause the wire to become hot.
3. Caution students not to touch the wire going to the nail or the wire on the nail, because the wire may become hot enough to cause a burn when connected to the battery.
4. Students should wear their safety goggles throughout this activity.

Materials

1. Use alkaline type batteries. Rechargeable batteries may become damaged by the currents involved in the experiment.
2. Do not use plastic covered wire as it can produce unpleasant odors if it becomes hot.
3. Enameled copper wire with a gauge between 16 and 24 is ideal.
4. An appropriate size for the nails is a 6 or 8 penny nail about 3 inches long.

Advance Preparation (20 minutes)

1. Test the batteries to determine that they are not discharged.
2. Cut enough pieces of wire for the class, each piece about 40 cm long, and remove the insulation from both ends of each piece.

Alternative Materials

If possible, have the battery in a holder with wires connected to the terminals of the holder rather than taped to the battery. C-cell batteries may be used in place of D-cell batteries and are less expensive and more readily available.

Procedure Tips

1. Caution students not to close the circuit for too long a time because, in addition to the possibility of getting hot, the nail may become magnetized and attract paper clips when the current is off.
2. Show students how to twist the wires together at the coil so that their coil does not come unwrapped or loose. Do not use tape to hold the coil in place.

Answers

1. Sample Answer: Some of the paper clips were attracted to the nail and were lifted up when the nail was pulled out of the container.
2. The paper clips fell away from the nail.
3. Look for answers that discuss the magnetic field generated around the nail. For example, in Step 3, the paper clips are attracted by the magnetic field produced by the current in the wire. When the device is disconnected in Step 4, the paper clips fall away because there is no current in the coil to produce a magnetic field to attract them.

Electricity, Magnetism, and Motion

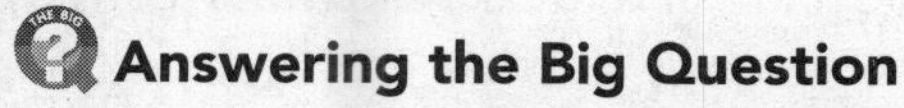

Answering the Big Question

The activities in this lesson will help students answer the Big Question by having them understand the relationship among electricity, magnetism, and motion; examine how a galvanometer works; and identify parts of an electric motor.

Inquiry Warm-Up

How Are Electricity, Magnets, and Motion Related?

Inquiry Focus

Predict—making an educated guess, based on observations, about the relative speed of two objects

Group Size Groups

Class Time 10 minutes

Alternative Materials

The rubber stoppers are not necessary as long as students are careful to rest one end of the tube on the floor.

Procedure Tips

Have a plastic tube ready to verify the statement made in Question 2.

Answers

1. Sample Answer: The steel slug falls faster; my prediction was correct.
2. Sample Answer: Copper is an electric conductor, while plastic is an electric insulator.
3. Look for answers that state that the current in the wire creates a magnetic field which can then interact with the magnet.

Quick Lab

Can a Magnet Move a Wire?

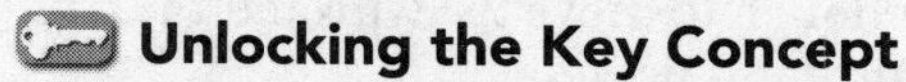

Unlocking the Key Concept

This activity will help students understand that a moving charge produces a magnetic field and that when a current-carrying conductor is placed into a magnetic field, the conductor moves, thus transforming electrical energy into mechanical energy.

Inquiry Focus

Draw Conclusions—analyzing the way a current-carrying wire and coil move when in the presence of a magnetic field in order to make a statement about how an electric current can produce mechanical motion

Group Size Pairs or groups

Class Time 15 minutes

Safety

Remind students to keep watches and other electronic devices away from the magnets.

Advance Preparation (15 minutes)

1. Assemble the magnetic field apparatus. For each magnetic field apparatus, you will need 1.5 m enameled copper wire, 20–24 gauge; insulated wire, 10–15 cm; wooden dowel, 3–4 mm in diameter, or round pencil; books; wooden or metal ruler; knife switch; 6-V battery. To assemble the apparatus wrap the enameled wire tightly around the dowel or pencil. Make sure to leave 20 to 30 cm of

wire free at both ends of the coil. Then, connect the battery to one end of the enameled wire. Connect the other end of the enameled wire to one terminal on the knife switch. Make sure the switch is in the open position before using the second piece of wire to connect the battery to the second terminal on the switch. Stack books, until a height of 10 inches is reached, at the lab stations. Place a ruler between the top two books so that 15 cm of the ruler is showing. Hang the wire coil from the ruler so that the coil is vertical above the table top. Remove the dowel or pencil from the coil of wire after placing the apparatus at the lab stations. For ease of storage replace the dowel or pencil in the wire after the activity to maintain the coils

2. Test the batteries to determine that they are not discharged.
3. Test your bar magnets to be sure they are strong enough to move the wire and the coil when current is flowing.

Alternative Materials

A ring stand and appropriate clamps and rods can be substituted for the books and ruler.

Procedure Tips

1. You may want to construct one or two of the magnetic field setups and place them as experiment stations. Have students rotate through the stations in pairs to conduct the experiment.
2. Caution students not to close the circuit for too long a time because the wire and or the coil may overheat, and they may also discharge the battery.
3. The bar magnet should be held perpendicular to the wire and parallel to the coil.

Answers

1. Sample Answer: Nothing happened when the switch was open. When the switch was closed, the wire moved toward the magnet or away from it depending on which pole was used.
2. Sample Answer: The coil twisted and swung farther as the magnet moved closer to the coil.
3. Sample Answer: The coil twisted and swung in the opposite direction when the magnet was reversed.
4. Look for answers that discuss the relationship between an electric current and the magnetic field it creates. For example, electric current in a wire creates a magnetic field that interacts with a magnet's magnetic field, and the interaction causes the wire to move. The coil interacts the same way but the interaction is stronger.

Quick Lab

How Galvanometers Work

Unlocking the Key Concept

This activity will help students understand how a galvanometer works.

Inquiry Focus

Make Models—using simple materials to construct a physical representation of how electric current and magnets interact within a galvanometer

Group Size Groups

Class Time 20 minutes

Safety

1. Students should wear the their safety goggles throughout this activity.
2. Caution students that the ends of the wires might be sharp and to take care while cutting the straw.

Advance Preparation (15 minutes)

To save time, you might wish to prepare the wires before class.

Alternative Materials

Other types of batteries may be used. Wire 18–24 gauge can be used.

Procedure Tips

You might wish to build a sample galvanometer in advance.

Answers

1. a magnetic field
2. Look for answers that discuss the interaction of the electric current and the resulting magnetic field. For example, the straw moved. The magnetic field around the wire interacted with the magnetic field around the magnets. The magnets moved, which moved the straw.

Quick Lab

Parts of an Electric Motor

Unlocking the Key Concept

This activity will allow students to assemble an electric motor and identify the parts of it.

Inquiry Focus

Design an Experiment—setting up a procedure to test how changing one factor affects the motion of the coil

Group Size Groups

Class Time 20 minutes

Safety

1. Students should wear their safety goggles throughout this activity.
2. Remind students that the ends of wires can be sharp.

Advance Preparation (15 minutes)

For each group, provide two paper clips in the shape shown below. You might wish to sand and prepare the wires before class.

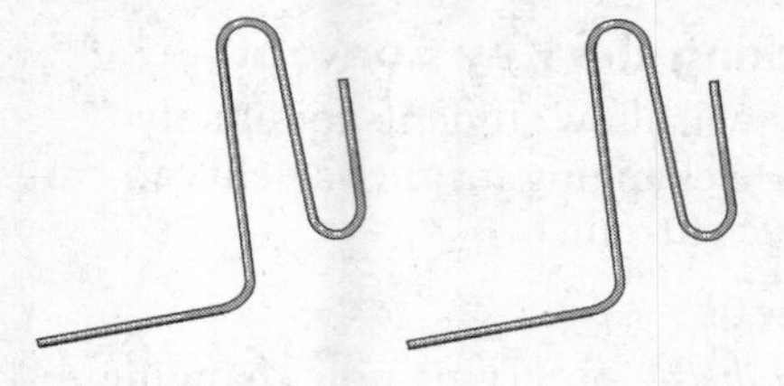

Alternative Materials

Any small cylindrical object, including a film canister, can be used in place of the battery for wrapping the wire in Step 1.

Procedure Tips

1. Students may not understand which half of the enamel to scrape off in Step 4. Before starting the lab, draw a picture on the board showing a side view of the wire. Draw a dotted line horizontally through the center of the wire. Instruct students to sand off the enamel above the dotted line at one end of the wire.
2. When creating their circuits, make sure students connect the exposed parts of the insulated wires to the paper clips.
3. Also make sure their wire loops have enough room over the magnet to spin freely. The students may have to give it a pretty good push to get it going.

Answers

1. a. paper clips; b. wire coil; c. the ends of the wire coil
2. Sample Answer: I could attach small fan blades on it so that the blades would spin and keep me cool.

Electricity From Magnetism

Answering the Big Question

The activities in this lesson will help students answer the Big Question by having them observe the production of electric current by the principle of electromagnetic induction and understand applications of that principle in generators and transformers.

Inquiry Warm-Up

Electric Current Without a Battery

Inquiry Focus

Develop a Hypothesis—using prior knowledge or experience to state the expected relationship that produces electric current when there is relative motion between a wire and a magnetic field

Group Size Groups

Class Time 10 minutes

Safety

1. Remind students that the ends of the wires might be sharp.
2. Caution students to keep the magnet away from watches and other electrical devices.

Advance Preparation

1. Cut enough wires for the number of setups you will be using, and remove the insulation from both ends of the wires.
2. To save time, set up the wires and galvanometer before the activity.

Procedure Tips

1. Tell students to keep the magnet away from their wristwatches and music players to prevent the devices from becoming magnetized.
2. If students do not get a meter reading, check that they are moving the wire in the correct direction, perpendicular to the magnetic field.
3. Use a mechanical multimeter, the type with a moving pointer. Most digital meters are too slow in their response to current changes.

Answers

1. A current is present in Steps 4 and 5.
2. The faster the wire moves, the greater the current is.
3. Sample Hypothesis: If a wire is moved between the poles of a magnet, then an electric current is produced.

Quick Lab

Inducing an Electric Current

Unlocking the Key Concept

This activity will show students that an electric current can be generated by a moving magnetic field.

Inquiry Focus

Develop a Hypothesis—making a testable statement about the effects of a moving magnetic field

Group Size Groups

Class Time 20 minutes

Safety

1. Students should wear their safety goggles throughout this activity.
2. Remind students that the ends of the wires are sharp.

Advance Preparation

Prepare enough wire for the groups in your class. Sand the ends of the wires to remove the coatings.

Alternate Materials

You can use a pre-built galvanometer or a handmade one such as the one from the Quick Lab "How Galvanometers Work."

Procedure Tips

1. Challenge students with steady hands to attempt to move the magnet and the coil of wire at the same speed, so that both are moving but no current registers. This drives home the fact that it is the relative change in the magnetic field, and not the existence of the field itself, that induces electric current.
2. Sample Hypothesis for Procedure Steps 3 and 5: If I move the magnet or coil back and forth, the galvanometer needle will move.

Answers

1. The needle moved back and forth. This indicates that current is flowing through the wire.
2. Sample Answer: Yes; I hypothesized that moving the wire coil around the magnet would create an electric current, and the galvanometer needle moved, showing that there was a current.

Quick Lab

How Generators Work

Unlocking the Key Concept

This activity will allow students to directly observe how a changing magnetic field can create an electric current.

Inquiry Focus

Control Variables—observing how changing one variable (the type of magnet) affects the generation of current and the brightness of the bulb

Group Size Groups

Class Time 20 minutes

Safety

1. Students should wear their safety goggles throughout this activity.
2. Remind students that the ends of the wire are sharp.
3. Remind students to keep watches and other electronic devices away from the magnets.

Advance Preparation (15 minutes)

1. Prepare the vial by wrapping the wire around the vial at least 350 times, leaving some loose wire at each end. For a $\frac{1}{2}$-inch vial, about 13 m of wire will be used.
2. To save time, sand the enamel coating off the ends of the wires before class. Prepare enough wires for each lab group.

Alternative Materials

Film canisters can be used instead of plastic vials.

Procedure Tips

Instruct students to keep the force and speed of their shaking constant.

Answers

1. Sample Answer: I changed the type of magnets in the tube. The bulb glowed brighter with the neodymium magnets than the regular magnets.
2. Look for answers that discuss how moving magnets create a changing magnetic field. The changing magnetic field induced an electric current in the wire.
3. Sample Answer: An advantage would be that the flashlight wouldn't need batteries. A disadvantage would be that you'd have to keep shaking it in order for it to stay on.

Quick Lab

How Transformers Work

Unlocking the Key Concept

This activity will help students make a model of a transformer.

Inquiry Focus

Calculate—using the ratio of loops in the primary coil to loops in the secondary coil to calculate the voltage through the secondary coil

Group Size Pairs or groups

Class Time 15 minutes

Alternative Materials

Instead of using spools of thread, students can use long pieces of string and actually wrap the string around the drinking straw to simulate wire being wrapped around an iron core.

Procedure Tips

Build one model in advance as an example for the students.

Answers

1. Coil B is the primary coil because it is connected to the voltage source.
2. 300 loops ÷ 600 loops = 0.5 100 volts ÷ volts in the secondary coil = 0.5
   The voltmeter would read 200 volts.

Name ______________________ Date ____________ Class ____________

Inquiry Warm-Up

10 min

Natural Magnets

When you think of magnets, you probably think of the things that hold papers to your refrigerator. However, there are many other materials that are magnetic.

INQUIRY FOCUS Observe

Procedure

1. Hold the magnet near the needle of the compass. Gently move the magnet and observe how the needle reacts.
2. Hold each of the rocks near the needle of the compass one at a time. Observe how the needle reacts each time.
3. Team up with two other groups. Place your compasses in a line with each compass touching the next. Make sure no rocks or magnets are near the compasses. Observe which way(s) the compass needles point.

Materials

magnet
compass
assorted rocks

Think It Over

1. How did the compass needle react to the magnet? Which rocks caused the compass needle to react in the same way?

____

____

____

2. Predict what would happen if you held these rocks near a small paper clip.

____

____

____

3. In Step 1, did the compass needles point in the same direction or in different directions? Recall that the needles move in response to magnets. What magnet could the needles be reacting to?

____

____

____

Name ______________________ Date __________ Class __________

PRE LAB

Detecting Fake Coins

Reviewing Content

Magnets were first discovered when people noticed that certain rocks and minerals had the ability to attract objects made of iron. Sometimes people try to cheat coin-operated vending machines by using steel washers or iron discs called slugs. Steel is mostly iron. Real U.S. coins are made from copper, nickel, and other metals that are not magnetic. Thus, real coins can be separated from magnetic metal slugs using a magnet. Nearly all vending machines have devices that can tell the difference between a real coin and a fake coin. They do this by checking magnetism, weight, and other properties of the object that was put into the machine. In this lab, you will see how the property of magnetism can be used to separate real coins from fake coins.

Reviewing Inquiry Focus

When you make predictions, you make an educated guess about what will happen during an event. An educated guess is not just an idea about the event. Instead, it is a guess based on observation and knowledge. Suppose you hold a ball in your hand and prepare to let it go. Predicting that the ball will change into a car is unrealistic—not an educated guess. Because you know about gravity and have seen objects fall, you would make the educated guess that the ball will fall to the ground.

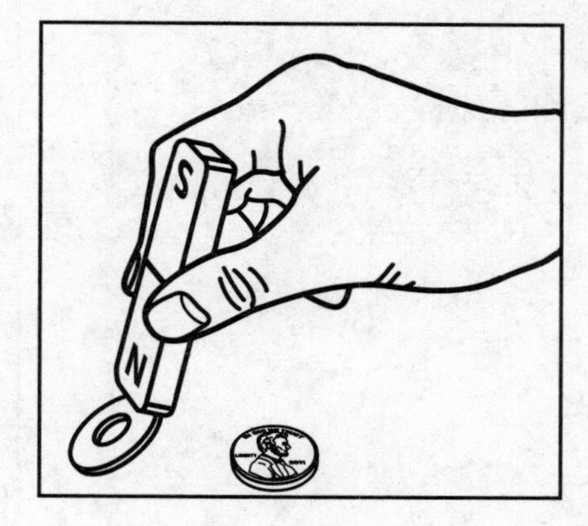

With these statements in mind, preview the Lab Investigation. Then answer the questions in the spaces provided.

1. What are some characteristics of coins and slugs by which a vending machine could detect one from the other?

____

____

2. Why is the bar magnet placed to one side of the center line of the cardboard?

____

____

Name ______________________ Date ____________ Class ____________

DIRECTED Inquiry

Detecting Fake Coins

Problem

How can you use a magnet to tell the difference between real and fake coins?

INQUIRY FOCUS
Predict

Materials

various coins
craft stick
tape
metric ruler
pencil
protractor
coin-size steel washers
small bar magnet, about 2 cm wide
thin, stiff cardboard sheet, about 25 cm × 30 cm

Procedure

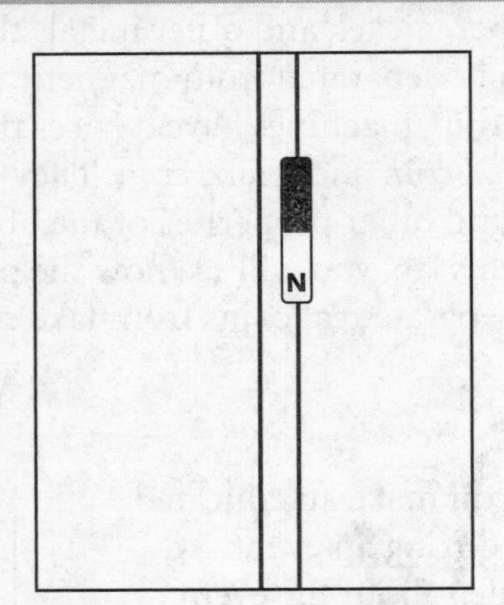

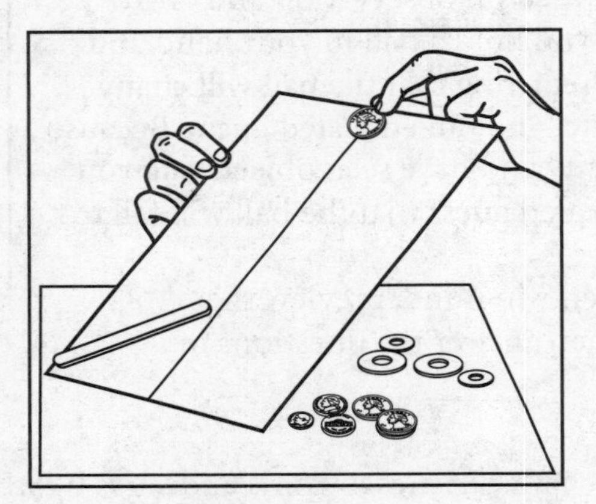

1. Use a pencil to label the front, back, top, and bottom of the piece of cardboard.
2. Measure to find the center of the cardboard.
3. Draw a line lengthwise down the middle of both sides of the cardboard.
4. On the back of the cardboard, draw a line parallel to and 2 cm to the right of the first line.

Name ______________________ Date______________ Class______________

DIRECTED Inquiry — Lab Investigation

DETECTING FAKE COINS *continued*

5. Place the magnet along the line you drew in Step 4, about one-third of the way down.
6. Tape the magnet in place as shown in the diagram on the previous page.
7. Place a craft stick on the front of the cardboard. The stick's upper end should be about 1 cm to the left of the center line and about 8 cm from the bottom of the cardboard.
8. Tape the stick at an angle, as shown in the diagram on the previous page.
9. Prop the cardboard against something that will hold it at an angle of about 45°. Throughout the experiment, use the protractor to check the angle of the cardboard. Adjust the cardboard if the angle changes.
10. Predict what will happen when you slide a coin down the front of the cardboard.

    ____

    ____

11. Place a coin on the center line and slide the coin down the front of the cardboard. *Hint: If the coin stops sliding, slowly increase the angle of the cardboard.*
12. Predict what will happen when you slide a steel washer.

    ____

    ____

13. Test your prediction by sliding a washer down the cardboard.
14. Once you have reached an angle at which the objects slide easily, send down a randomly mixed group of coins and washers one at a time.

Name ______________________ Date ______________ Class ______________

DIRECTED Inquiry — **Lab Investigation**

DETECTING FAKE COINS *continued*

Analyze and Conclude

1. **Predict** Explain your predictions from Steps 10 and 12.

2. **Observe** Describe how observations made during the lab either supported or did not support your predictions.

3. **Infer** What is the role of the magnet in this lab?

4. **Draw Conclusions** What can you conclude about the metals from which the coins and washers are made?

5. **Control Variables** Why does the steepness of the cardboard affect how the coin separating device works?

6. **Evaluate the Design** Canadian coins contain iron. Would this device be useful in Canada to detect fake coins? Explain.

Name ______________________ Date ____________ Class ____________

DIRECTED Inquiry • **Lab Investigation**

POST LAB

Detecting Fake Coins

1 **Relate Evidence and Explanation** Describe what you saw as real coins and fake coins slid down the cardboard. How can you explain what happened?

____

____

____

____

2 **Predict** Some countries have coins that are made of aluminum or brass, a combination of zinc and copper. Do you think your device could be used in those countries to separate real coins from iron slugs? Explain.

____

____

____

3 **Summarize** Describe what you learned about the magnetic properties of U.S. coins and iron slugs and how those properties can be used to separate coins from slugs. List any questions you still have.

What I learned ____

____

____

____

What I still want to know ____

____

____

____

Communicate

Evaluate the Impact on Society Write a brochure that explains how the device could be used to separate real coins from fake coins and what advantages it might have for vending machine owners. Make sure your brochure contains information explaining the difference between materials that are magnetic and those that are not.

Name _______________ Date _______________ Class _______________

OPEN Inquiry

Detecting Fake Coins

Problem

INQUIRY FOCUS
Observe, Develop a Hypothesis

How can you use a magnet to tell the difference between real and fake coins?

Materials

- various coins
- various coin-size steel washers
- tape
- metric ruler
- protractor
- small bar magnet, about 2 cm wide
- thin, stiff piece of cardboard, about 25 cm × 30 cm
- craft sticks
- straws
- pencils
- rubber bands
- tongue depressors

Design an Experiment

1. In this activity, you will explore how magnets are used to separate coins from other metal objects. You will create a set-up similar to a vending machine that separates the coins from the washers by utilizing magnetism.
2. First you will practice using the magnet. Take the cardboard provided by your teacher and tape the magnet lengthwise to the back, somewhere in the middle of the top third of the cardboard.
3. Write a hypothesis that predicts how the path of the coins and washers will be affected by the magnet.

   ____

   ____

4. Hold the cardboard at an angle. Practice sliding a few coins and washers down the cardboard and notice their reactions to the magnet. Use these observations to design a system that separates the coins and metals washers into individual piles.
5. Your teacher has provided some materials that may help you with your design, but it is your choice which materials you choose to use. Use the notebook on the next page to draw a diagram of the device you design. Be sure to include labels, arrows, and descriptions on your diagram.
6. Have your teacher review and approve your design. Then run your experiment and record your observations in a data table.

DETECTING FAKE COINS *continued*

7. Consider the following questions if you need to troubleshoot problems in your design.

   a. How does the thickness of the cardboard make a difference in the strength of the magnet?

   b. Is the path that the coins and washers are sliding along on the face of the cardboard too close or too far from the magnet?

   c. How does the angle of the cardboard affect the speed with which the objects pass the magnet? Is this speed so fast that it overpowers the magnetic pull on the objects?

   d. What materials are available to make a directed path for the coins and washers to separate into individual piles?

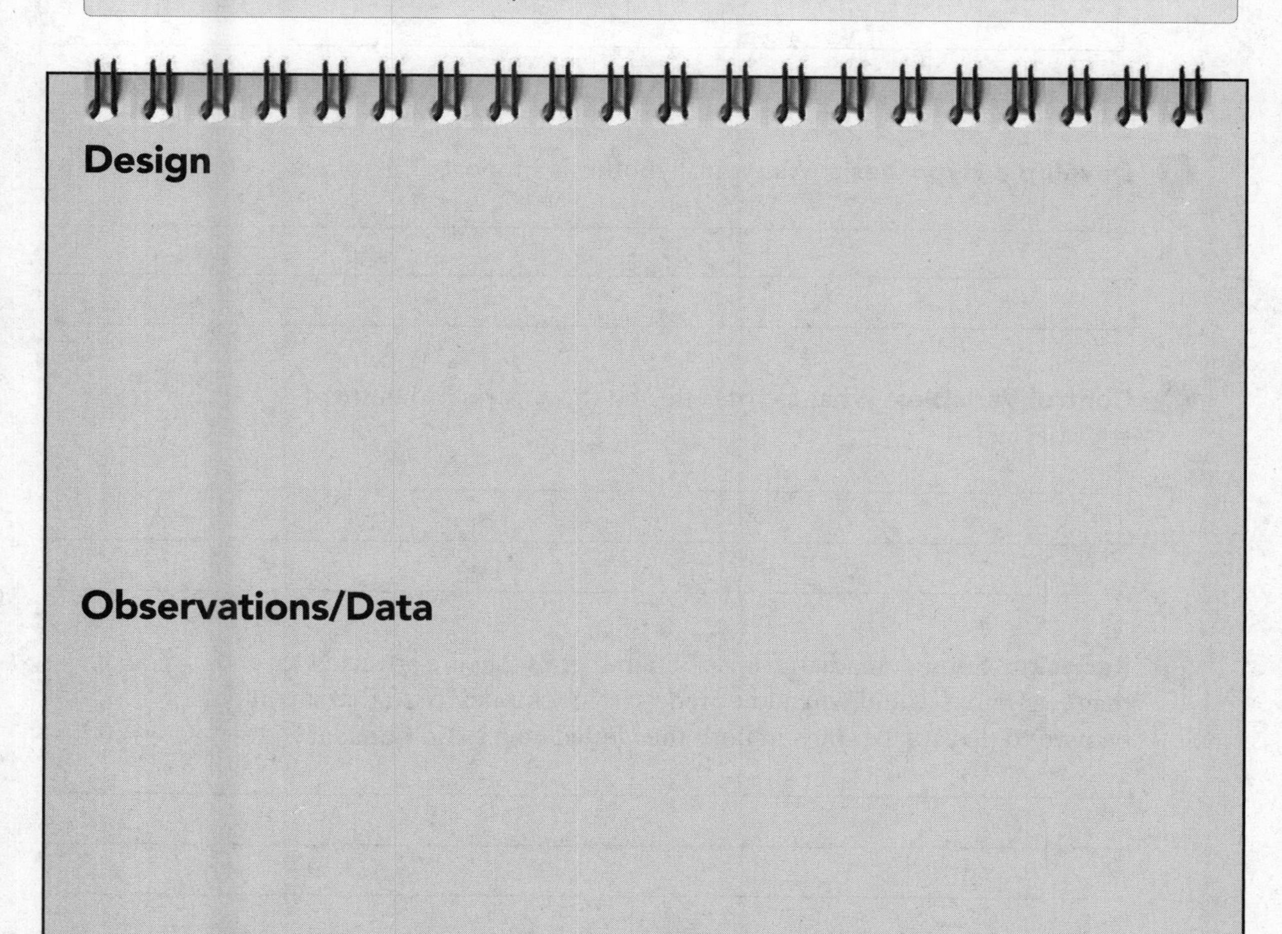

DETECTING FAKE COINS *continued*

Analyze and Conclude

1. **Observe** What is the role of the magnet in your device?

2. **Relate Evidence and Explanation** How did the magnet affect the path of the washers and coins as they slid down the cardboard?

3. **Develop a Hypothesis** Was your hypothesis supported? Explain.

4. **Control Variables** What factors affected the success or failure of your device?

5. **Redesign** Some Canadian coins contain metals that are attracted to magnets. What would you add or redesign in your device so that it could be used to detect fake coins in both the United States and Canada?

Name ______________________ Date ____________ Class ____________

OPEN Inquiry — Lab Investigation

POST LAB

Detecting Fake Coins

1. **Troubleshoot** What changes did you have to make to your original design in order to make it work to separate the coins from the slugs?

____

____

2. **Design a Solution** Imagine you owned an arcade. How would you design a token that could be used in coin-operated video games that use magnets?

____

____

3. **Identify a Need** Magnetism can be used to separate other magnetic and non-magnetic objects besides coins and slugs. Describe a real-world application where a device similar to the one you built could be used.

____

____

4. **Summarize** Describe what you learned about the magnetic properties of U.S. coins and iron slugs and how those properties can be used to separate coins from slugs. List any questions you still have.

What I learned ____

____

What I still want to know ____

____

Communicate

Design a Solution Imagine you are a vending machine salesman. Make a computer presentation for a group of snack food business executives that demonstrates why your machines are the best at detecting and rejecting fake coins. Feel free to improve upon your existing device's design by applying materials and machinery that aren't available in your lab. Be sure to discuss:

- different ways that your machine detects and rejects fake coins
- trials you conducted to minimize and correct errors while designing your machine
- the effect of magnetism on real coins versus slugs

Name ______________________ Date ____________ Class ____________

Quick Lab — 15 min

Magnetic Poles

Which end is north? Which end is south? In this activity, you will attempt to determine the north and south poles of a magnet.

INQUIRY FOCUS Draw Conclusions

Procedure

1. Tape a labeled magnet onto each of the cars. Make sure that the "A" end is facing the front of one car and the "B" end is facing the front of the other car.
2. Place the cars about 15 cm apart with the fronts of the cars facing each other. Roll the cars toward each other. Observe how the cars react.
3. Flip one of the magnets around so that both cars have end "B" facing forward. Roll the cars toward each other again. Observe how the cars react.
4. Replace one of the labeled magnets with a blank magnet. Roll the two cars toward each other. Observe how the cars react.

Materials

- two toy cars
- tape
- two bar magnets, with ends labeled "A" and "B"
- bar magnet without labels

Think It Over

1. Based on your observations, what can you determine about the polarities of sides "A" and "B" of the magnets?

____

____

____

2. Explain how you can use your observations from Step 4 to correctly label the sides of your blank magnet.

____

____

____

3. From your observations, can you determine the north and south poles of your magnets? If not, what could you use to make that determination?

____

____

____

Name ______________________ Date __________ Class __________

Inquiry Warm-Up

Predict the Field

You may have heard about the "magnetic field" or "electric field" around an object. These fields are invisible, but with the right materials you can see how they are shaped.

INQUIRY FOCUS Predict

Procedure

1. Predict how the iron filings will line up when the magnet is placed under the petri dish.

   ____

   ____

Materials

petri dish with iron filings
magnet

2. Lay the magnet on a flat surface and place the petri dish on top of it.
3. Make a sketch of the magnet and the pattern formed by the iron filings.
4. Trade sketches with two other groups that used magnets that weren't shaped like your magnet. Observe the shapes of the magnetic fields.

Think It Over

1. Explain why this experiment would not work with plastic shavings instead of iron filings.

   ____

   ____

2. How does the magnetic force on a metal object change as the object gets closer to the magnet? Explain how the distances between the iron filings could be related to the strength of the magnetic force.

   ____

   ____

   ____

Name ______________________ Date ____________ Class ____________

Quick Lab

Spinning in Circles

A compass is a small magnet that can pivot or turn freely. In this activity, you will use a compass to determine the shape of a magnetic field and come to some conclusions about the way a compass works.

INQUIRY FOCUS Draw Conclusions

Procedure

1. Place the bar magnet in the center of a sheet of paper.
2. Place the compass about 2 cm beyond the north pole of the magnet. Draw a small arrow next to the compass showing the direction of the compass needle.
3. Repeat Step 2, placing the compass at 20 to 30 different positions around the magnet.
4. Remove the magnet and observe the pattern of arrows you drew.

Materials

- bar magnet
- sheet of paper
- pencil
- compass

Think It Over

1. What does your pattern of arrows represent?

____

____

2. How does the direction of the arrows at the poles compare to the direction halfway between the poles?

____

____

____

3. Do compasses respond only to Earth's magnetic field? Explain your answer.

____

____

____

____

Name ______________________ Date ____________ Class ____________

Quick Lab

Earth's Magnetic Field

You are standing in a giant magnetic field right now–Earth's! In this activity, you will make a model of Earth's three-dimensional magnetic field.

INQUIRY FOCUS **Make Models**

Procedure

1. Use the funnel to pour a spoonful of iron filings into the soda bottle.
2. Insert the bar magnet into the plastic test tube. Tie one end of the string to one end of the test tube and snap on the cap.
3. Lower the test tube into the bottle until one end is resting on the center of the bottom. Drape the string over the mouth of the soda bottle, making sure the test tube does not move, and close the cap tightly.
4. Look through the side of the bottle. Draw the magnet and the arrangement of the iron filings in the left box below.
5. Hold up the bottle, but don't shake the contents. Look through the bottom of the bottle. Draw the magnet and filings in the right box below.

Materials

- bar magnet
- plastic test tube w/snap cap
- string, 15 cm
- soda bottle with cap
- iron filings
- funnel

Think It Over

1. If you could see Earth's magnetic field, which view of Earth would look like Step 4—looking down at the North Pole or looking at a side view of the Western Hemisphere? Explain.

   ____

   ____

2. Where is Earth's magnetic field stronger, at the equator or at the poles? Use your observations from this experiment to support your answer.

   ____

   ____

Name ______________________ Date__________ Class__________

Inquiry Warm-Up — 15 min

Electromagnetism

In 1820, H. C. Oersted discovered that a current flowing through a wire produces a magnetic field. This effect is an example of electromagnetism.

INQUIRY FOCUS Infer

Procedure

1. Place the Oersted apparatus on a flat surface. Make sure the switch is open.
2. Place three compasses at different positions centered under the wires on the apparatus as shown in the diagram.
3. Observe the direction in which each of the compasses is pointing.
4. Close the switch. Observe the compasses.
5. Open the switch to stop the current. Then close it again. Observe the compasses.

Materials

Oersted apparatus (two 16–20-gauge insulated wire [20–30-cm length], 1.5-V light bulb in holder, D-cell battery in holder, knife switch, wooden board [optional])

3 compasses

Think It Over

1. What happened to the compasses when a current flowed through the wire?

____

____

2. How do you know that current was flowing through the wire?

____

____

3. What can you infer about electricity and magnetism?

____

____

Name ______________________ Date ____________ Class ____________

Quick Lab

Electric Current and Magnetism

Electric currents have magnetic fields. In this activity, you will determine the relationship between electric current and magnetism.

INQUIRY FOCUS Infer

Procedure

1. Use the tape to label one end of the wire "A" and the other end "B." Leave room at both ends so the wire can be attached to the battery. Tape the center part of the wire to a table.
2. Attach the "A" end of the wire to the positive terminal of the battery and the "B" end of the wire to the negative terminal of the battery.
3. Put the compass on the table near the center of the wire. Observe which way the needle points.
4. Detach the wires from the battery. Turn the battery around and reattach the wires so that the "A" end is now attached to the negative terminal and the "B" end is now attached to the positive terminal.
5. Observe which way the needle points.

Materials

- 16-gauge copper wire, 45 cm
- masking tape
- 6-V battery
- compass

Think It Over

1. Whenever the wire was attached to the battery, a current ran through the wire. What changed when you changed how the wire was attached to the battery?

____

____

2. What happened to the compass needle after the current in the wire changed?

____

____

3. What can you infer about the relationship between electric current and magnetism?

____

____

____

Name ______________________ Date ____________ Class ____________

Quick Lab — 15 min

Magnetic Fields From Electric Current

Compasses won't always point toward Earth's magnetic north pole. Electric current can cause a compass to point in a different direction!

INQUIRY FOCUS Interpret Data

Materials

- 6-V battery
- wire, 16–18-gauge coated copper wire, 30 cm
- 2 wire leads with alligator clips
- compass (magnetic)
- compass (drawing)
- small box (18 × 14 × 11 cm) with one small hole in the top of the box and one small hole in the side of the box

Procedure

1. Using the small hole in the top of the box as the center, set the drawing compass to 2 cm and draw a circle on the top of the box. On the circle, mark where the numbers 3, 6, 9, and 12 would be if the circle was a clock face.
2. Thread the wire through the holes in the box. Make sure both free ends of the wire are outside of the box.
3. Using the wire leads, attach the ends of the wire to the terminals of the battery.
4. Place the magnetic compass on one of the numbers you marked on the circle in Step 1 so that the compass is outside the circle, but just touching it. In the corresponding circle below, draw an arrow that shows how the compass needle is pointing at that number.
5. Pick a different number on the circle and place the magnetic compass there. On the corresponding circle at the right, draw an arrow that shows how the compass needle points at that spot.
6. Remove the wire leads from the battery.

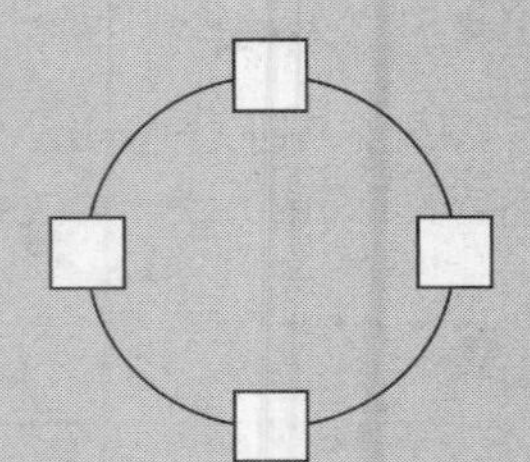

Think It Over

1. A compass needle lines up with a magnetic field. Use your data to find the magnetic field pattern around a current-carrying wire. Describe this pattern.

____

____

2. What would happen to the compass needles if you switched off the current?

____

____

Name ____________________ Date __________ Class __________

Quick Lab

Electromagnet

A current flowing through a wire creates a magnetic field around the wire. The field can be concentrated, or intensified, by wrapping the wire around an iron object. In this activity, you will create an electromagnet.

INQUIRY FOCUS Infer

Procedure

1. Tightly wrap the piece of insulated copper wire around a nail 10–12 times.
2. Tape one end of the wire to a battery terminal.
3. Hold one end of the nail and touch the other end of the wire to the other battery terminal. Quickly dip the nail into a container of paper clips. Slowly lift the nail above the container.
4. Pull the wire away from the battery terminal and observe what happens.

Materials

- 1 m insulated copper wire
- electrical tape
- iron nail
- D-cell battery
- container of steel paper clips

Think It Over

1. What happened in Step 3 when you dipped the nail into the paper clips and then pulled the nail away?

____

____

2. What happened when you pulled the wire away from the battery in Step 4?

____

____

3. What explanation can you give for what you observed in Step 3 and Step 4?

____

____

____

____

Name ______________________ Date__________ Class__________

Inquiry Warm-Up

How Are Electricity, Magnets, and Motion Related?

You have already seen how electrically charged or magnetic objects can make other objects move. In this activity, you will see another way magnetism can affect motion.

INQUIRY FOCUS Predict

Procedure

Materials

copper tube w/ rubber stopper at one end
steel slug
magnetic slug
stopwatch

1. Predict whether the magnetic slug or steel slug will take less time to fall through the copper tube.

   ____

2. Rest the closed end of the tube on the floor. Have one person from your group hold the tube straight up. Have another person drop the metal slug down the tube while a third person times how long it takes for it to fall to the bottom. Record the time. __________

3. Repeat Step 2 with the magnetic slug. Record the time. __________

Think It Over

1. Which slug took less time to fall? Was your prediction correct?

   ____

   ____

2. If you used a plastic tube, neither slug would have fallen faster than the other. What might be the important difference between copper and plastic? *Hint: Think about electric currents.*

   ____

   ____

3. Magnets can cause other magnets to move. Explain how a magnet could cause a wire to move when the wire has current running through it.

   ____

   ____

   ____

Name ______________________ Date ____________ Class ____________

Quick Lab

Can a Magnet Move a Wire?

Electric motors produce mechanical motion from electric current. In this activity, you will investigate how an electric current can produce mechanical motion and draw some conclusions about how this is possible.

INQUIRY FOCUS Draw Conclusions

Procedure

1. Your teacher will supply a set up for this lab and show you how to use it.
2. With the switch open, slowly move one pole of a bar magnet toward one of the wires supporting the coil and observe what happens. Switch magnet poles and repeat.
3. Close the switch and repeat Step 2. Then immediately open the switch.
4. Hold a bar magnet parallel to the coil several centimeters away. Close the switch briefly and observe the coil. Observe what happens as you move the magnet closer.
5. Reverse the direction of the magnet and repeat Step 4.

Materials

bar magnet
magnetic field apparatus

Think It Over

1. What happened each time you moved the magnet near the wire in Steps 2 and 3?

____

____

2. What happened when you moved the magnet closer to the coil?

____

____

3. Was anything different when you reversed the magnet in Step 5? Explain.

____

____

4. What can you conclude from your observations?

____

____

Name ______________________ Date ____________ Class ____________

Quick Lab

20 min 

How Galvanometers Work

Galvanometers use the relationship between electric current and magnetic fields to move a needle, measuring the strength of the current. In this activity, you will build a model galvanometer.

INQUIRY FOCUS Make Models

Materials

drinking straw
scissors
sandpaper
round coffee stirrer
2 cylindrical ceramic magnets (1-cm diameter)
1.25 m of magnet wire
250-mL beaker
D-cell battery and holder

Procedure

1. Use the sandpaper to scrape off the insulation around the ends of the wire.
2. Pinch down about 2.5 cm of the straw to make it flat. Cut about 2 cm through the middle of this section, making sure to go through both layers of plastic.
3. Separate the two halves of the straw to make a "V" shape. Lay the coffee stirrer inside the "V" at right angles to the straw. Center the coffee stirrer in the straw.
4. Pinch the cut end of the straw shut. Put one magnet on each side of the straw to hold it shut.
5. Wrap the wire around the beaker four times, leaving several centimeters of wire free on both ends. Twist the wire to keep it tight around the beaker.
6. Balance the coffee stirrer on the rim of the beaker so that the magnets are suspended over the center of the beaker and the straw is pointing up.
7. Attach the ends of the wire to the metal clips of the battery holder. Observe what happens to the straw.

Think It Over

1. When you connected the wire to the battery holder, a current ran through the wire. What does an electric current running through a wire create?

____

____

2. What did you observe in Step 7? Explain why this happened.

____

____

Name ______________________ Date __________ Class __________

Quick Lab

Parts of an Electric Motor

Electric motors are used in all sorts of everyday devices, from blenders to cars. In this activity you will use a few items to build a simple motor.

INQUIRY FOCUS Design an Experiment

Procedure

1. Wrap the enamel-coated wire around the battery to make a wire coil. Leave about 5 cm free at each end. Remove the battery.
2. Wrap the free ends of the wire 3 or 4 times around the coil to keep it from unwinding. The 2 free ends should be directly across from each other on the coil.
3. Use the sandpaper to scrape the enamel from a 2-cm length at one end of the wire coil.
4. Scrape the enamel from just one side of the wire at the other end of the coil.
5. Use clay to anchor the short ends of the paper clips to the table. Position the clips so that they are standing up with the small U-shapes parallel to each other.
6. Place the free ends of the wire coil in the U-shapes of the paper clips. Make sure the coil is balanced and the free ends of the wire stick straight out from the coil.
7. Use the remaining clay to anchor the magnet under the wire coil. *Note: You may need to build a small pedestal with the clay.*
8. Attach the alligator clip end of a wire lead to each of the paper clips.
9. Attach the free ends of the wire lead to the terminals of the battery. Give the coil a gentle push and observe what happens next.

Materials

- D-cell battery and holder
- 2 large reshaped paper clips
- 1 m of enamel-coated 22–24 gauge wire
- permanent disk magnet
- pliers
- sandpaper
- 3 grape-sized pieces of clay
- 2 wire leads with alligator clips
- 1 D-cell holder

Think It Over

1. Next to the name of each motor part, write what you used to make that part (or a similar one) in the motor you just built.

   a. Brushes __________ b. Armature __________ c. Commutator __________

2. How could you modify this motor to make it do useful work?

   ____

   ____

Name ______________________ Date ____________ Class ____________

Inquiry Warm-Up — 10 min

Electric Current Without a Battery

Induction is one way to produce an electric current in a wire. This activity will allow you to observe the production of electric current without a battery.

INQUIRY FOCUS Develop a Hypothesis

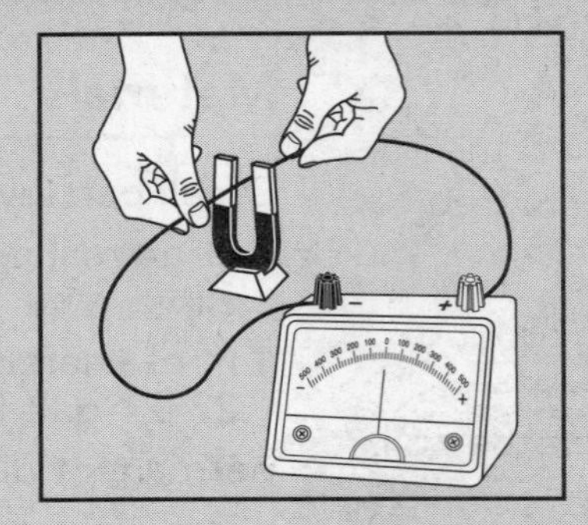

Materials

- 1 m insulated copper wire
- galvanometer or multimeter
- horseshoe magnet
- clay

Procedure

1. Connect the wire to the terminals of a galvanometer or a multimeter.
2. Set a horseshoe magnet on a surface so that the open end faces up and use modeling clay to hold it in place.
3. Hold the wire between the poles of the horseshoe magnet. Observe the meter.
4. Move the wire up and down between the poles. Observe the meter.
5. Move the wire faster, and again observe the meter.

Think It Over

1. In which steps does the meter indicate a current is present?

____

____

2. What can you say about the current produced and how fast the wire moves?

____

____

3. Propose a hypothesis to explain why a current is present. Use an "If . . . then. . . ." statement.

____

____

Name ______________________ Date ____________ Class ____________

Quick Lab

Inducing an Electric Current

You have already seen how an electric current can generate a magnetic field. In this activity, you will see how a magnetic field can be used to generate an electric current.

INQUIRY FOCUS Develop a Hypothesis

Procedure

Materials

enameled copper wire, 32-gauge
bar magnet
galvanometer

1. Twist the wire into a coil with 10–20 loops. The diameter of the coil should be wider than the magnet.
2. Connect the ends of the coil to the galvanometer.
3. Insert the magnet into the coil. Hypothesize what will happen if you hold the coil still and move the magnet in and out.

   ____

   ____

4. Test your hypothesis and observe what happens to the galvanometer needle.
5. Write a hypothesis about what will happen if you hold the magnet still and move the coil back and forth over the magnet.

   ____

   ____

6. Test your hypothesis from Step 5 and observe the needle.
7. Make sure the galvanometer needle is at rest. Keep the magnet within the wire coil, but now hold both the magnet and the coil still. Observe the needle.

Think It Over

1. What happened to the needle in Step 4? What does this indicate about the wire?

   ____

   ____

2. Did your results in Step 6 support your second hypothesis? If so, explain why. If not, develop a hypothesis that would be supported by your results.

   ____

   ____

Name ______________________ Date ____________ Class ____________

Quick Lab

20 min

How Generators Work

You may think of generators as large machines in electric power plants. However, you can build a generator that fits in the palm of your hand.

INQUIRY FOCUS Control Variables

Procedure

1. Using a pair of scissors, gently scrape the ends of the wire to remove the coating. Attach the ends of the wires to the connecting points on the bulb to make a complete circuit.
2. Put three regular disc magnets in the vial. Use the cap to seal the vial.
3. Shake the vial. Observe the bulb.
4. Uncap the vial and switch out the regular disc magnets with the neodymium magnets.
5. Shake the vial again. Observe the bulb.

Materials

- plastic vial with cap
- three disc magnets, 10–12-mm
- neodymium magnets, 10–12-mm
- enameled copper wire, 26–32–gauge
- jumbo LED, 10-mm
- scissors

Think It Over

1. Which variable did you change over the course of this experiment? How did changing the variable affect your observations and results?

____

____

____

2. Explain how shaking the tube caused a current to flow in the wire.

____

____

____

3. Name at least one advantage and at least one disadvantage of a flashlight operated by this kind of generator.

____

____

____

____

Name ______________________ Date ____________ Class ____________

Quick Lab

How Transformers Work

Large transformers help electricity get from a generating plant to your home. Small transformers help you charge electronic devices.

INQUIRY FOCUS Calculate

Procedure

1. Fold the drinking straw into a square. Crease the corners so the square can hold its shape.
2. Unfold the straw. Slide the spools onto the straw.
3. Fold the straw back into a square, making sure the spools are on opposite sides of the square.
4. Use the tape and marker to label the spools "Coil A: 600 coils" and "Coil B: 300 coils." Label the cups "Voltmeter A," "Voltmeter B," and "Voltage Source."
5. Use small pieces of modeling clay to attach two pieces of string to Coil A and two pieces of string to Coil B.
6. Take the free ends of the strings attached to Coil A. Use small pieces of modeling clay to attach the ends of the strings to Voltmeter A.
7. Take the free end of one of the strings attached to Coil B. Use a small piece of modeling clay to attach the end of the string to Voltmeter B.
8. Take the free end of the other string attached to Coil B. Use a small piece of modeling clay to attach the end of the string to the Voltage Source.
9. Use small pieces of modeling clay and the last piece of string to connect the Voltage Source to Voltmeter B.

Materials

1 plastic drinking straw
2 spools of thread
3 small paper cups
5 15-cm pieces of string
1 2-inch square of modeling clay
tape
marker

Think It Over

1. In your model, is Coil B the primary coil or the secondary coil? How do you know?

____

____

2. The number of loops in the primary coil divided by the number of loops in the secondary coil equals the voltage in the primary coil divided by the voltage in the secondary coil. If the voltmeter attached to the primary coil read 100 volts, what would the voltmeter attached to the secondary coil read?

____

____

Common SI Units

Measurement	Unit	Symbol	Equivalents
Length	1 millimeter 1 centimeter 1 meter 1 kilometer	mm cm m km	1,000 micrometers (µm) 10 millimeters (mm) 100 centimeters (cm) 1,000 meters (m)
Area	1 square meter 1 square kilometer	m^2 km^2	10,000 square centimeters (cm^2) 1,000,000 square meters (m^2)
Volume	1 milliliter 1 liter	mL L	1 cubic centimeter (cm^3 or cc) 1,000 milliliters (mL)
Mass	1 gram 1 kilogram 1 ton	g kg t	1,000 milligrams (mg) 1,000 grams (g) 1,000 kilograms (kg) = 1 ton
Time	1 second	s	
Temperature	1 Kelvin	K	1 degree Celsius (°C)

Metric Conversion Tables

When You Know	Multiply by	To Find			
		When You Know	Multiply by	To Find	
inches feet yards miles	2.54 0.3048 0.914 1.609	centimeters meters meters kilometers	0.394 3.281 1.0936 0.62	inches feet yards miles	
square inches square feet square yards acres square miles	6.45 0.093 0.836 0.405 2.59	square centimeters square meters square meters hectares square kilometers	0.155 10.76 1.196 2.471 0.386	square inches square feet square yards acres square miles	
cubic inches cubic feet cubic yards	16.387 0.028 0.765	cubic centimeters cubic meters cubic meters	0.061 35.315 1.31	cubic inches cubic feet cubic yards	
fluid ounces quarts gallons	29.57 0.946 3.785	milliliters liters liters	0.0338 1.057 0.264	fluid ounces quarts gallons	
ounces pounds tons	28.35 0.4536 0.907	grams kilograms metric tons	0.0353 2.2046 1.102	ounces pounds tons	

When You Know		
Fahrenheit	subtract 32; then divide by 1.8	to find Celsius
Celsius	multiply by 1.8; then add 32	to find Fahrenheit

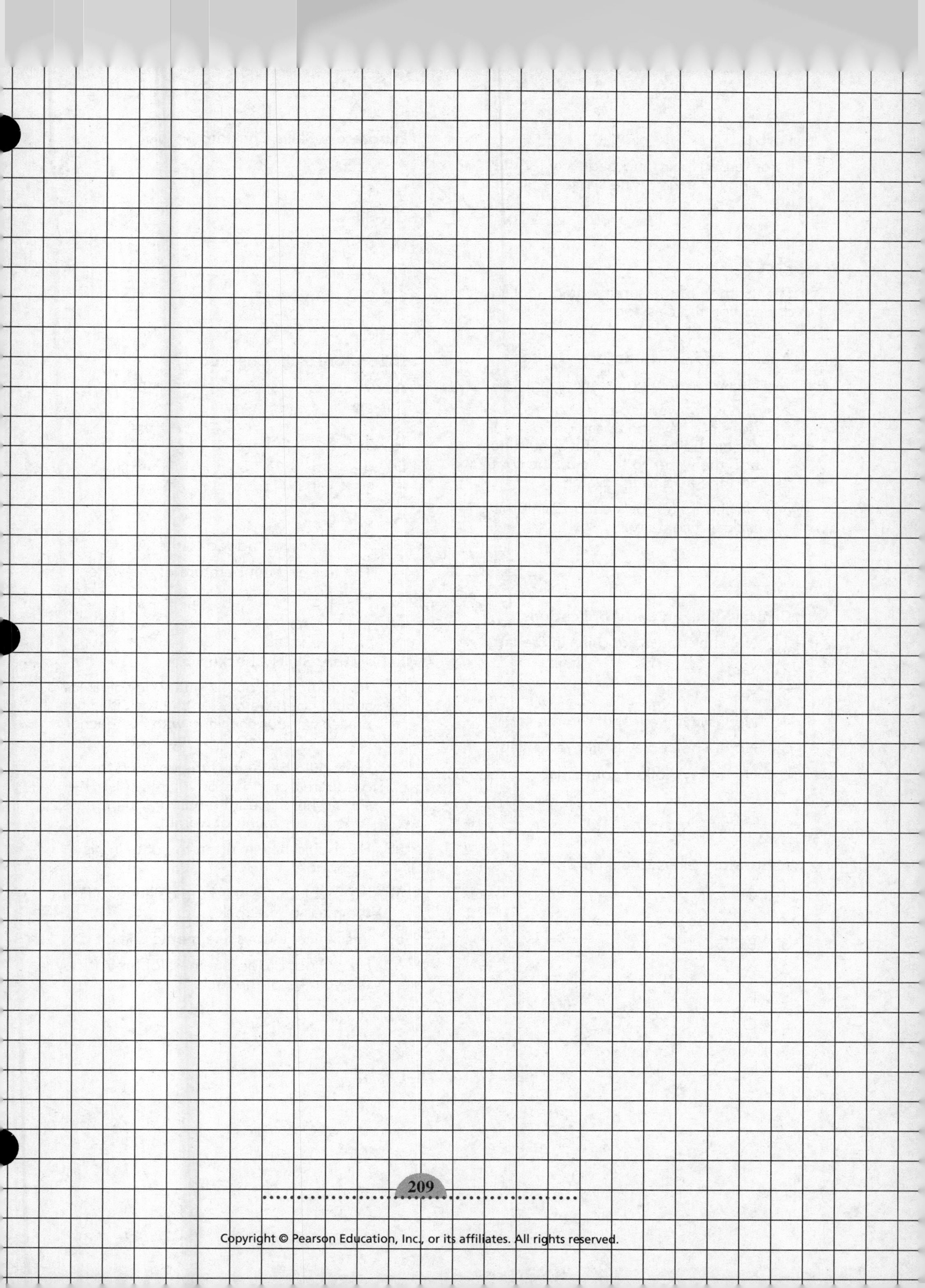

STUDENT SAFETY TEST ANSWERS

p. xxviii

Part 1

Refer to page xxiv and page xxv for the meanings of each of the symbols.

p. xxix

Part 2

The location of the safety equipment will depend on the classroom.

Analyze and Conclude

1. He is not wearing safety goggles.
2. She is not wearing safety goggles. She does not have an apron on. Her hair should be tied back. She should not add the water to the acid. She should add the acid to the water.
3. He should not be heating something in a closed container.

p. xxx

Critical Thinking and Applications

1. No; she should not drink in the lab.
2. Yes
3. Yes
4. No; always wear shoes in the lab.
5. No; no horseplay is allowed in lab.
6. No; always follow correct lab procedures.

p. xxxii

Laboratory Skills Checkup 2

1. A
2. E
3. B
4. G
5. F
6. C
7. D

p. xxxiii

Laboratory Skills Checkup 3

A. 7

B. 5

C. 8

D. 6

E. 1, 2

F. 2, 3, 4

p. xxiv

Laboratory Skills Checkup 4

A. 9

B. 5

C. 4, 7, 8

D. 6

E. 1

F. 6, 7

G. Amount of salt added to the water

H. The freezing temperature of the water

p. xxxv

Laboratory Skills Checkup 5

1. He did not put on his safety goggles. He should not have broken the rock into two pieces without checking with his teacher first.
2. He should have used the units on the graduated cylinder for volume. Also, he should have used the unit gram for mass. An ounce is a unit of weight.
3. He should have written the data in his notebook.
4. He should have used the balance to find the mass of the rock.
5. In science, always use metric units.
6. He did not divide the mass of the rock by the volume of the rock.